100 GAMES
OF LOGIC

W9-BSV-203

Also by Pierre Berloquin

---

100 Perceptual Puzzles
100 Numerical Games

Pierre Berloquin

100 GAMES OF LOGIC

Foreword by Martin Gardner
Drawings by Denis Dugas

BARNES
&NOBLE
BOOKS
NEW YORK

Copyright © 1977 by Pierre Berloquin

This edition published by Barnes & Noble, Inc.,
by arrangement with Scribner, an imprint of Simon & Schuster

All rights reserved. No part of this book may be used or reproduced
in any manner whatsoever without the written permission of the Publisher.

1995 Barnes & Noble Books

ISBN 1-5661-9701-5 *casebound*
ISBN 0-7607-1396-0 *paperback*

Printed and bound in the United States of America

        02 MC 9
        02 MP 9 8 7 6

FG

Contents

Foreword	ix
Problems	1
Solutions	105

Foreword

Pierre Berloquin, who put together this stimulating and delightful collection of mind benders, is a clever young Frenchman who was born in 1939 in Tours and graduated in 1962 from the Ecole Nationale Supérieure des Mines in Paris. His training as an operations research engineer gave him an excellent background in mathematics and logical thinking.

But Berloquin was more interested in writing than in working on operations research problems. After two years with a Paris advertising agency, he decided to try his luck at free-lance writing and this is how he has earned his living since. In 1964 he began his popular column on "Games and Paradoxes" in the magazine *Science et Vie* (Science and Life). Another column, "From a Logical Point of View," appears twice monthly in *The World of Science*, a supplement of the Paris newspaper *Le Monde*. Occasionally he contributes to other French magazines. One of his favorite avocations is leading groups of "*créativité*," a French cocktail of brainstorming, synectics, and encounter therapy, for the discovery of new ideas and the solution of problems—a logical extension of his interest in puzzles.

Berloquin's published books are *Le Livre des jeux* (card and board games), *Le Livre des divertissements* (party games), *Le jeu de Tarot* (Tarot card game), *Testez votre intelligence* (intelligence tests), *100 grandes réussites* (solitaire games), *Un souvenir d'enfance d'Evariste Galois* (Memoir of the Childhood of Evariste Galois); he is co-author of *Voulez-vous jouer avec nous* (Come Play with Us) and *100 jeux de cartes classiques* (card games).

This volume is Berloquin's own translation into English of one of his four paperback collections of brainteasers which have been enormously popular in France and Italy since they were published in Paris in 1973. This one is concerned only with logical puzzles. The other three contain numerical, geometrical, and alphabetical problems. Denis Dugas, the graphic artist who illustrated all four books, is one of the author's old friends.

The puzzles in this collection have been carefully selected or designed (many are original with the author or artist) so that they will not be too difficult for the average reader who is not a mathematician to solve, and at the same time not be *too* easy. They are all crisply, clearly given, accurately answered at the back of the book, and great fun to work on whether you crack them or not.

At present, Berloquin is living in Neuilly, a Paris suburb, with his wife, Annie, and their two children.

MARTIN GARDNER

100 GAMES
OF LOGIC

PROBLEMS

Game 1

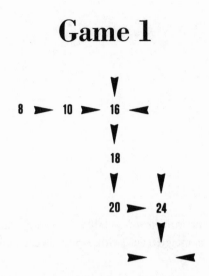

What number belongs in the empty space between the three arrows?

Game 2

Two bars of iron lie on a table. They look identical, but one of them is magnetized (with a pole at each end), and the other is not.

How can you discover which bar is magnetized if you are only allowed to shift them on the table, without raising them and without the help of any other object or instrument?

Game 3

These words follow a logical progression:

        SPHINX
        LISTEN
        TALION

Which of these could be next?

        AUREOLE
        SPROUT
        IODINE
        PROTON

Game 4

The four drawings about the duel are not in the right order. Please correct.

Game 5

A	B	C	D
E	F	G	H
I	J	K	L
M	N	O	

← P

This first diagram is incomplete. Obviously, the letters are entered in alphabetical order, so the empty square gets a P.

The second diagram has been filled according to a different logical principle. Which letters go in the empty squares?

A	C	E	
L	N		I
J		M	K
	F	D	B

? ↗

Game 6

These words belong to the same logical family:

> BASSOON
> ADDRESS
> CORRALLED
> SUCCESSIVE
> FOOTHILL

Which of these words does too?

> NEEDLESS
> PERIPHERAL
> MULTISYLLABIC
> WALL

Game 7

If LEAH is LOUIS's sister,
if CLARISSE is BRUNO's sister,
if MAUD is CHRISTOPHER's sister,
then who is HAMILTON's sister—

IRENE, CLAIRE, SUE, or PEGGY?

Game 8

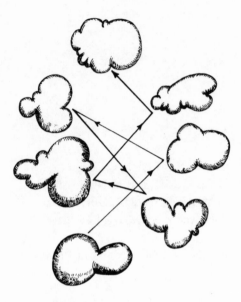

The first illustration shows how seven clouds can be placed in logical order: the first cloud has two curves; the second, three curves; and so on up to eight curves.

In the second illustration the logical principle is not too different from the first. Can you discover it? Show the logical wig sequence with arrows.

Game 9

These words follow a logical progression:

> DRAMA
> RABBI
> CYCLE
> IDLED
> TENSE
> AFFIX

Which of these could be next?

> HATCH
> FLUTE
> MEDIA
> WIGGLE

Game 10

The family gathering consists of father, mother, son, daughter, brother, sister, cousin, nephew, niece, uncle, and aunt. But only two men and two women are present. They have a common ancestor, and there has been no consanguine marriage.

Explain.

Game 11

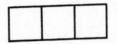

Find a common English three-letter word, knowing that:

LEG has no common letter with it.
ERG has one common letter, not at the correct place.
SIR has one common letter, at the correct place.
SIC has one common letter, not at the correct place.
AIL has one common letter, not at the correct place.

Game 12

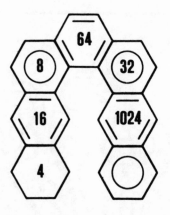

What number belongs in the empty circle?

Game 13

Five of the flowers in the vase belong to the same logical family. One is an intruder—which one, and why?

GAMES OF LOGIC

Game 14

Timothy's tie rack boasts 17 blue ties, 11 yellow, 9 orange, 34 green, and 2 violet, not sorted by color.

The light bulb has burned out. Timothy cannot see what color the ties are.

How many ties does Timothy have to take to be sure he has at least two ties of the same color?

Game 15

These words follow a logical progression:

ABROAD
BLONDE
LANCER
ACCORD
CHORDS

Which of these could be next?

HARASS
HERPES
OLDISH
MARKER

Game 16

An accident has just occurred. The drawings are out of order—please correct.

Game 17

```
C A B C A B
B A B C A C
A C A B B A
C B A C C B
B A C B A C
C B A C B A
```

The letters are arranged according to a logical principle. What principle?

Game 18

These words belong to the same logical family:

> UNDECEIVABLE
> SIMULTANEOUS
> ALIMENTATION
> CAUTIOUSNESS
> GLADIATORIAL
> FORAMINIFERA

Which of these words does too?

> PHILANTHROPY
> SEISMOLOGIST
> ONOMATOPOEIA
> REAPPEARANCE

Game 19

You have been been playing "heads or tails" and you discover that your opponent is cheating. He chooses heads most of the time, for his coin has two heads.

Knowing this, you bet enough to win your money back in one more toss of his. You don't want to take the risk of demonstrating that he is a cheater. So what do you do to win?

Game 20

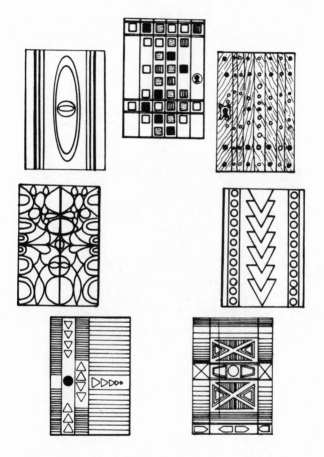

As in Game 8, there is a logical principle by which the seven doors can be put in order.

What is it? What order should they be in?

Game 21

These words follow a logical progression:

> SUNKEN
> MONASTICISM
> TUESDAY
> WEDGIES
> THUMB-SUCKER
> FRIVOLITY

Which of these could be next?

> SQUANDER
> SATIATE
> MINE
> TABLE

Game 22

Find a common English four-letter word, knowing that each of these four words have two letters in common with it, which are not at the correct places:

EGIS
PLUG
LOAM
ANEW

Game 23

Six of the houses belong to the same logical family. One is an intruder—which one, and why?

GAMES OF LOGIC

Game 24

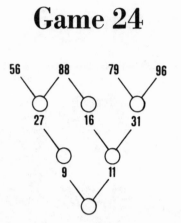

56   88   79   96
   27   16   31
      9   11

What number belongs below the bottom circle?

Game 25

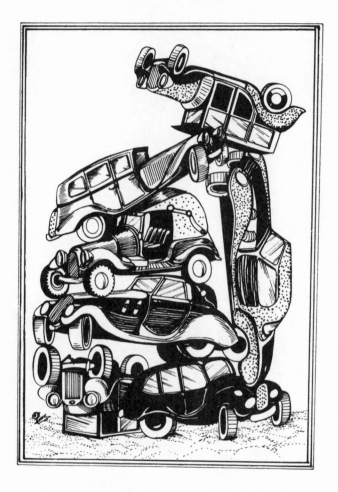

Six of the cars belong to the same logical family. One is an intruder—which one, and why?

GAMES OF LOGIC

Game 26

An inflatable boat is floating in a swimming pool. Which will raise the water level higher:

Throwing a coin into the boat?
Throwing a coin into the water?

Game 27

These words follow a logical progression:

BOXER
ELATE
RATER
OLIVE
HOTEL
ALIVE

Which of these could be next?

DUCAL
IMAGE
HASTE
MEANS

Game 28

Timothy is at the barber's. The drawings are out of order
—please correct.

Game 29

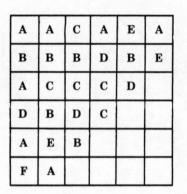

A	A	C	A	E	A
B	B	B	D	B	E
A	C	C	C	D	
D	B	D	C		
A	E	B			
F	A				

← ?

Can you complete the square logically?

Game 30

These words belong to the same logical family:

> ACREAGE
> LEGEND
> CARPENTER
> MACERATION
> CARMINE
> SURFACE
> TENANT

Which of these words does too?

> LIMITATION
> ASHORE
> MANNER
> NEED

Game 31

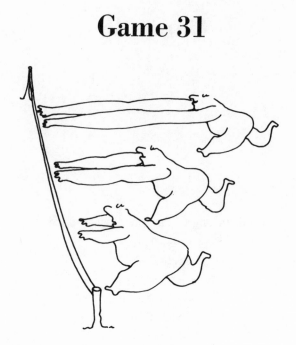

Every morning Timothy, Urban, and Vincent run cross-country before breakfast.

After a month they realize that Timothy has finished before Urban more often than after him and that Urban has finished before Vincent more often than after him.

Is it possible that Vincent has finished before Timothy more often than after him?

Game 32

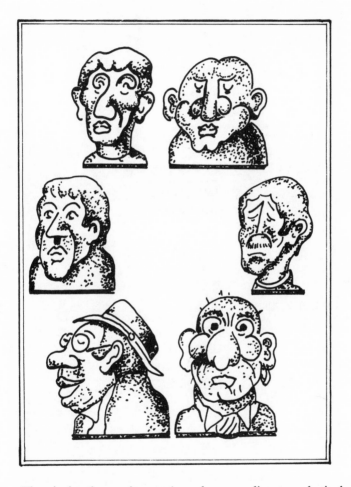

The six heads can be put in order according to a logical principle.

What is it? What order should they be in?

Game 33

These words follow a logical progression:

> TRUSTFUL
> SALTWORT
> TOMORROW
> OFFENDER
> EXERTION
> ROYALIST

Which of these could be next?

> PEDIGREE
> HYPNOTIC
> ARTERIAL
> JUDGMENT

Game 34

Find a common English five-letter word, knowing that:

ADULT has two letters in common with it, not at their correct places.

GUSTO has no common letter with it.

STORY has one common letter, at the correct place.

BUILT has one common letter, at the correct place.

DYING has one common letter, not at the correct place.

BUGLE has two common letters, but only one at the correct place.

LIGHT has no common letter with it.

Game 35

Five friends, Andrew, Bernard, Claude, Donald, and Eugene, each have a son and a daughter. Their families are so close that each has married his daughter to the son of one of his friends, and as a result the daughter-in-law of the father of Andrew's son-in-law is the sister-in-law of Bernard's son, and the son-in-law of the father of Claude's daughter-in-law is the brother-in-law of Donald's daughter.

But although the daughter-in-law of the father of Bernard's daughter-in-law has the same mother-in-law as the son-in-law of the father of Donald's son-in-law, the situation is simplified by the fact that no daughter-in-law is the sister-in-law of the daughter of her father-in-law.

Who married Eugene's daughter?

Game 36

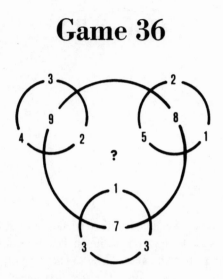

What number belongs in the center?

Game 37

Timothy notes that his five best friends do not know one another. To get things started he invites three of them to lunch: Adams, Brown, and Carter. (The two other friends are Dickinson and Emerson.) The five first names are, in no particular order, Alex, Bob, Chip, Dave, and Elmer.

After the lunch Timothy lists the results:
- Bob still does not know Brown.
- Chip knows Adams.
- Dave knows only one of the others.
- Elmer knows three of the others.
- Alex knows two of the others.
- Dickinson knows only one of the others.
- Emerson knows three of the others.

What is the full name of each of the five?

Game 38

A man sits on a buoy floating in a swimming pool. In his right hand is a glass containing an ice cube. If he throws the ice cube into the swimming pool, when will the water level rise?

- When the cube falls into the water?
- Or not until the cube is completely melted?

Game 39

These words follow a logical progression:

> TOOTHSOME
> FORECAST
> SIXTINE
> ATONAL

Which of these could be next?

> SUMMER
> BOAT
> TENDERNESS
> TYPICAL

Game 40

Andrew, Bernard, Claude, Donald, and Eugene have summer houses along the Atlantic coast.

Each wanted to name his house after the daughter of one of his friends—that is, Anne, Belle, Cecilia, Donna, and Eve (but not necessarily in that order).

To be sure that their houses would have different names the friends met to make their choices together.

Claude and Bernard both wanted to name their house Donna. They drew lots and Bernard won. Claude named his house Anne.

Andrew named his house Belle.

Eve's father hadn't come, and Eugene phoned to tell him to name his house Cecilia.

Belle's father named his house Eve.

What is the name of each friend's daughter? What is the name of his house?

Game 41

1	1	8
2	5	13
3	21	

← ?

Can you complete the square logically?

Game 42

These words belong to the same logical family:

        AFGHAN
        INDEFINITELY
        SYNOPSIS
        STUPENDOUS
        BURST

Which of these words does too?

        GLACIAL
        COMPANION
        RESCRIPT
        HIJACKER

Game 43

At an international conference there are twenty-one who speak French, twenty-one who speak English, and twenty-one who speak German. But there are much fewer than sixty-three conferees, since some of them speak several languages. In fact, all the possibilities are represented: some speak one language, some speak two, and some speak all three.

If those who speak a specific language are called a group, then, within that group, those who speak a specific two languages (like those who speak only that language, and those who speak all three languages) are called a subgroup.

Each subgroup of a given group contains a different number of persons (at least three). The largest subgroup is made up of those who speak only French.

How many speak English and German but not French?

Game 44

The seven vases can be put in order according to a logical principle.

What is it? What order should they be in?

Game 45

These words follow a logical progression:

> AUSTRALIA
> RAISIN
> CREASE
> PATOIS
> VIRTUOSO

Which of these could be next?

> MAIN
> SCHISM
> GRANITOID
> GENEROUS

Game 46

- No strategist, if he is a good tactician, can lose a battle.
- An audacious strategist does not fail to have the confidence of his troops.
- No bad tactician has the confidence of his troops.
- Women despise only the vanquished.

If the preceding statements are taken as true, can an audacious strategist be despised by women?

Game 47

Six men, A, B, C, D, E, and F, for short, and their mothers live in a village.

Each mother was widowed and has married as her second husband one of the men other than her son.

Mrs. D points out to C's mother that, by marriage, she (Mrs. D) has become the great-grandmother of Mrs. E, A has become B's stepgrandfather, and Mrs. F is the daughter-in-law of Mrs. C's granddaughter-in-law.

Who married whom?

Game 48

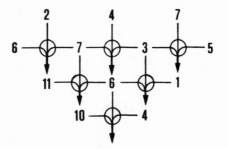

What number belongs under the bottom arrow?

Game 49

Five friends with suitable names—Doe, Deer, Hare, Boar, and Roe—are coming back from a hunting party with five animals of the same names; each has killed one animal, *not* corresponding to his own name, and each has missed another differently named animal, again not corresponding to his own name.

- The deer was killed by the hunter who has the name of the animal killed by Roe.
- The doe was killed by the hunter who has the name of the animal missed by Hare.
- Deer, who missed a roe, was very disappointed to kill only a hare.

Who killed what?

Game 50

An Oriental prince, a great lover of chess, is on his death-bed and worries about the fate of his immense fortune. To which of his three sons should it go?

His fortune is in the form of a chess set made of diamonds and rubies.

He decides that his fortune will go to the son who plays exactly half as many games of chess as the prince has days left to live.

The oldest son refuses, saying he does not know how long his father will live.

The second son refuses for the same reason.

The youngest son accepts. How does he respect his father's desires?

Game 51

These words follow a logical progression:

> PHILOSOPHICOSOCIOLOGICALLY
> ZOO
> CHRONOGRAMMATICAL
> QUOTE
> EAGLE
> ENTERTAINED
> KISS
> DISENTANGLEMENT
> OCCULTISM

Which of these could be next?

> SCALP
> INCEST
> TAWDRY
> VALETUDINARIANISM

Game 52

The drawings of a motorcyclist repairing his machine are out of order—please correct.

Game 53

1	1	1	1
1	3	5	7
1	5	13	25
1	7	25		← ?

Can you complete the square logically?

Game 54

These words belong to the same logical family:

> CHINK
> TRANCE
> STAIN
> CHIME
> TUBA
> PERK

Which of these words does too?

> GERMANE
> EMBARGO
> BANANA
> NIGHTMARE

Game 55

Six of the shoes belong to the same logical family. One is an intruder—which one, and why?

Game 56

These words follow a logical progression:

ACE
TAB
COG
ADD
EAR
RAF
GUT
UGH
IVY
TAJ

Which of these could be next?

KID
BOY
ASK
TOO

Game 57

After a long trip abroad, Timothy makes the following statements about the hotels he patronized:

1. When the food is good, the waitresses are gracious.
2. No hotel open all the year long fails to have a view of the ocean.
3. The food is bad only in some cheap hotels.
4. Hotels which have a swimming pool carefully cover their walls with honeysuckle.
5. The hotels where the waitresses are discourteous are those that are open only part of the year.
6. No cheap hotel accepts dogs.
7. Hotels without a swimming pool have no view of the ocean.

In these hotels, can a dog owner enjoy honeysuckle?

Game 58

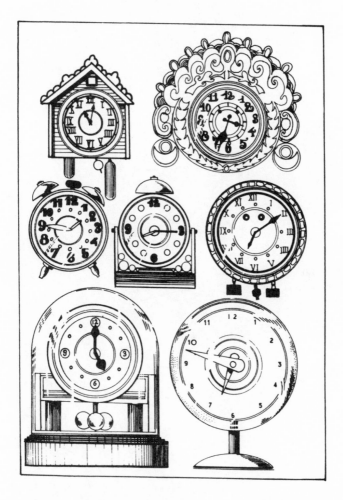

Six of the clocks belong to the same logical family. One is an intruder—which one, and why?

Game 59

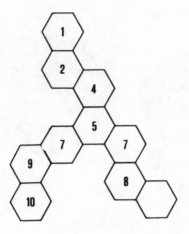

What number belongs in the empty hexagon?

GAMES OF LOGIC

Game 60

Lebrun, Lenoir, and Leblanc are, not necessarily in that order, the accountant, warehouseman, and traveling salesman of a firm.

The salesman, a bachelor, is the shortest of the three.

Lebrun, who is Lenoir's son-in-law, is taller than the warehouseman.

Who has what job?

Game 61

These words follow a logical progression:

> ADIEU
> IDIOM
> EIGHT
> UNIPOLAR
> PRODUCT
> TRUCKLER

Which of these could be next?

> PAROCHIALISM
> EPISPASTIC
> STRICTNESS
> OSTEOLOGIC

Game 62

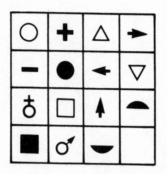

Can you complete the square logically?

Game 63

These words belong to the same logical family:

CALCIFEROUS
CUPELLATION
EDUCATION
LACTIFEROUS
OUTDISTANCE
PNEUMONIA

Which of these words does too?

ZYMOTICALLY
ABSTEMIOUS
UNAPOSTOLIC
MEDALLION

Game 64

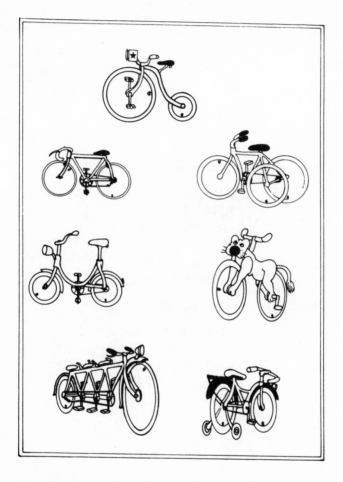

The seven cycles can be put in order, beginning with the starred one on top, according to a logical principle.

What is it? What order should they be in?

Game 65

These words belong to the same logical family:

> ADJUNCTIVELY
> AMBIDEXTROUS
> DEMONSTRABLY
> GLANDIFEROUS
> HYPNOTIZABLE
> QUESTIONABLY

Which of these words does too?

> VERSIFICATOR
> DIVARICATION
> STENOGRAPHIC
> EXPOSTULATES

Game 66

Smith is a butcher and president of the street storekeepers' committee, which also includes the grocer, the baker, and the tobacconist. They all sit around a table.

- Smith sits on Smyth's left.
- Smythe sits at the grocer's right.
- Psmith, who faces Smyth, is not the baker.

What kind of store does Smythe have?

Game 67

A driver makes the following statements about automobiles:

- A front-wheel drive gives a good hold on the road.
- It is necessary for a heavy car to have good brakes.
- Any powerful car is high-priced.
- Light cars do not have a good hold on the road.
- A low-powered car cannot have good brakes.

Is it logical for this driver to accept a cheap front-wheel drive?

GAMES OF LOGIC

Game 68

What number belongs under the bottom right circle?

Game 69

Six of these people belong to the same logical grouping. One does not—which one, and why?

GAMES OF LOGIC

Game 70

A history test had three questions on presidents of the United States. Here are the answers of six students:

1. Polk, Polk, Taylor.
2. Taylor, Taylor, Polk.
3. Fillmore, Fillmore, Polk.
4. Taylor, Polk, Fillmore.
5. Fillmore, Taylor, Taylor.
6. Taylor, Fillmore, Fillmore.

Every student answered at least one question correctly. What are the correct answers?

Game 71

After a holdup, four bank employees give descriptions of the robber.

According to the guard, he had blue eyes, was tall, and was wearing a hat and a vest.

According to the cashier, he had dark eyes, was short, and wore a vest and a hat.

According to the secretary, he had green eyes, was medium-sized, and wore a raincoat and a hat.

According to the director, he had gray eyes, was tall, and wore a vest but no hat.

It was later determined that each witness described only one detail out of four correctly. Every detail was described correctly by at least one witness.

What is the correct description of the criminal?

Game 72

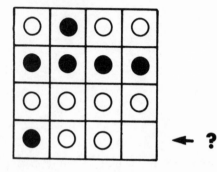

← ?

Can you complete the square logically?

Game 73

An explorer is in a country where everyone lives either on the plain or in the mountains. They speak the same language, but the dwellers on the plain always tell the truth while those from the mountains always lie.

The explorer knows little about the language. He knows that "Grb" and "Mnl" mean yes and no but does not know which is which.

He asks three inhabitants of the country two questions each:

- Are both the others from the plain?
- Are both the others from the mountains?

They all answer "Grb" to both questions, except for one who answers "Mnl" to the second question.

What does "Grb" mean?

Game 74

These words belong to the same logical family:

> CODIFY
> LAMINA
> STOVE
> RESET
> JOKUL
> QUIRES

Which of these words does too?

> REST
> GRAIL
> STOIC
> ORDEAL

Game 75

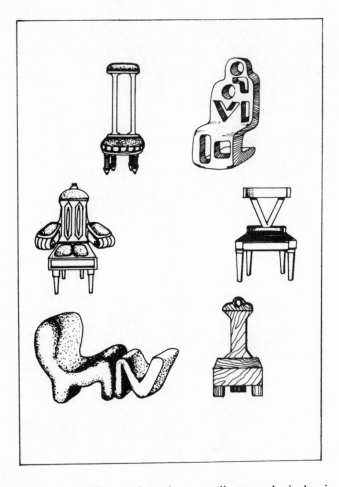

The seats can be put in order according to a logical principle.

What is it? What order should they be in?

GAMES OF LOGIC

Game 76

Timothy has been abandoned by his electrician and must finish the wiring of his new house alone.

He courageously tries to untangle the labyrinth of wires already laid down. He is particularly worried about three wires of the same color going from the basement to the attic. He wants to identify them, labeling both the basement and attic ends of one wire A, of another wire B, and of the last wire C.

His only tool is a meter that shows if current is passing through a length of wire or not when both ends of the wire are attached to the meter. Thanks to it, Timothy only needs to make one round trip between basement and attic to complete the labeling. Explain how he does it.

Game 77

Four couples spend an evening together. Their first names are Elizabeth, Jeanne, Mary, Anne, Henry, Peter, Louis, and Roger.

At a given time:

- Henry's wife is not dancing with her husband, but with Elizabeth's husband.
- Roger and Anne are not dancing.
- Peter is playing the trumpet, with Mary at the piano.

If Anne's husband is not Peter, who is Roger's wife?

Game 78

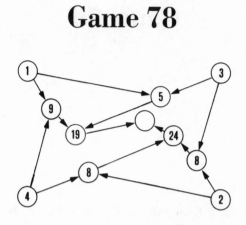

What number belongs in the empty circle?

Game 79

In the small town hall the five members of the council, Anthony, Bernard, Claude, David, and Edwin, are about to elect one of them mayor.

They sit in alphabetical order clockwise around the table.

In the first round everyone votes for the one who votes for his neighbor on the left. Of course, no one is elected. But who voted for whom?

Game 80

These words belong to the same logical family:

> TRANSUBSTANTIATION
> CRYSTALLOGRAPHICAL
> STRAIGHTFORWARDLY
> PHILANTHROPICALLY
> PARTICULARIZATION
> MALADMINISTRATION

Which of these four words does too?

> DISPROPORTIONABLE
> INCOMMUNICABILITY
> MARSIPOBRANCHIATE
> DEMONSTRATIVENESS

Game 81

A company whose cash is kept in a strongroom is owned by three associates whose confidence in one another is very limited. They decide to put several locks on the door and to distribute the keys among themselves so that:

- No associate can open the door alone.
- Any two associates can pool their keys to open the door.

How many locks do they need and how many keys?

Game 82

- Some mathematicians are philosophers.
- Immortals are ignorant of philosophy.
- No poet practices mathematics.
- All mortals are poets.

Are these four assertions logically compatible?

Game 83

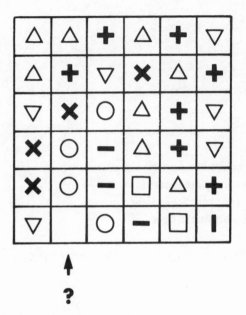

Can you complete the square logically?

GAMES OF LOGIC

Game 84

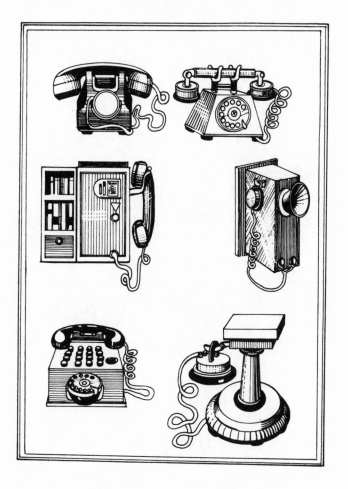

The six telephones can be put in order according to a logical principle.

What is it? What order should they be in?

Game 85

These words belong to the same logical family:

FIRST
DEFY
BELLOW
CHINTZ
DEIST
FILMY
HORSY
KNOT
ABBOT
BEGIN

Which of these words does too?

ABDOMEN
LOW
EDIBLE
LOYAL

Game 86

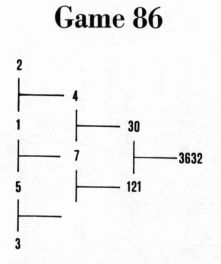

What number belongs in the empty space at the foot of the second column?

Game 87

Six of the portraits belong to the same logical family. One is an intruder—which one, and why?

Game 88

A general is choosing a cook from 625 volunteers. He orders them to form a 25 × 25 square. He orders the tallest man in each row to step aside and chooses the shortest of the twenty-five.

Then he changes his mind and has them go back to their places. He orders the shortest man in each column to step aside and chooses the tallest of *these* twenty-five.

The two cooks chosen by the two methods are different. Which one is taller?

Game 89

These words follow a logical progression:

> JANEY
> FEBRILE

Which of these could be next?

> BEZOAR
> PAVILION
> MAROON
> SEPARATE

Game 90

The staff of a bank includes a director, an assistant director, and four department heads. The director wants to have several locks on the strongroom door and several keys, so that:

- He can open the door alone.
- The assistant director can open it only if he is accompanied by any one of the department heads.
- Any three department heads can open it.

How many locks are needed, and how should the keys be distributed?

Game 91

- Incompetence excludes wisdom.
- Hope can only be founded on knowledge.
- Violence is the last refuge of incompetence.
- To know anything, one must possess wisdom.

What can be deduced about violence from these four assertions?

Game 92

These words belong to the same logical family:

> DIFFICULT
> HUBBUB
> FALLACIOUSLY
> ANTICORROSIVE
> PARAGRAMMATIST
> HOLLOWLY

Which of these words does too?

> SYNTACTICALLY
> INDISCREETNESS
> DEFENDER
> ANNALS

Game 93

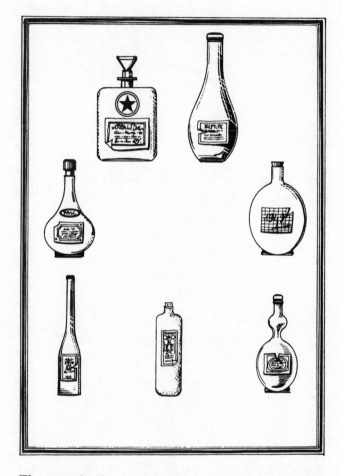

The seven bottles can be put in order, beginning with the starred one and its neighbor to the right, according to a logical principle.

What is it? What order should they be in?

Game 94

Four fishermen, Al, Bert, Claude, and Dick (not necessarily respectively), own boats called "Mary Jean," "Susie-Q," "The Big One," and "Seagull."

Unfortunately the fishermen do not know one another as well as they think they do. Each sentence spoken by a fisherman is true only when it is entirely or partly about his own boat. Otherwise it is false.

Al says: "My boat, 'Susie-Q,' and 'Seagull' are the only ones with radios on board."

Bert says: "Claude is lucky to have one of the three boats with a radio."

Claude says: " 'Seagull' is Al's boat."

Dick says: "I have never been on 'Seagull' or 'Mary Jean.' "

Who owns which boat?

Game 95

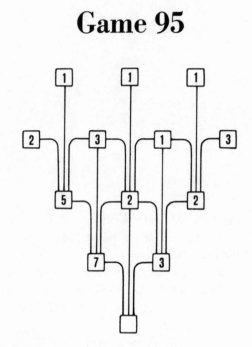

What number belongs in the empty square?

GAMES OF LOGIC

Game 96

Six of the robots belong to the same logical family. One is an intruder—which one, and why?

Game 97

The staff of a bank includes a director, two assistant directors, and five department heads.

The director wants several locks on the strongroom door and several keys so that:

- He can open the door alone.
- An assistant director can only open it together with the other assistant director, *or* with any two department heads.
- Any four department heads can open it.

How many locks are needed and how should the keys be distributed?

Game 98

An explorer is in a country with two villages, a big one and a small one. Although they all speak the same language, the inhabitants of the small village never lie, while those of the big village always lie.

The explorer speaks to a child, pointing to a man and a woman.

"Is the village of this man bigger than the village of this woman?"

"Grb."

"Is your village bigger than the village of this man?"

"Grb."

You don't know whether Grb means yes or no. In fact, you don't need to know. But can you tell what is the correct answer to each question?

Game 99

A plane was returning from the Olympic Games with five athletes who placed first through fifth in an event. They made the following statements:

A: "I was not the last."

B: "C was third."

C: "A was behind E."

D: "E was second."

E: "D was not the first."

On account of modesty or for some other reason, the gold and silver medalists lied. The three worst athletes told the truth.

What order did they all place in?

Game 100

Andrew, Bernard, and Claude are bicycling. Each one is riding the bicycle of one friend and wearing the hat of another.

The one who wears Claude's hat is riding Bernard's bicycle.

Who is riding Andrew's bicycle?

SOLUTIONS

Game 1

30: every arrow adds 2.

Game 2

Take either bar and push one end against the middle of the other bar, forming a T.

If the magnetized bar is the top of the T, there is no pull on the other bar.

Game 3

IODINE: six-letter words with one, two, three, four vowels.

Game 4

Let us call the four drawings:

A B
C D

D precedes A and C: the monk's jug has not yet been knocked down.

A precedes C, where the white-booted musketeer is putting his wine-stained hat back on.

B precedes D: the black-booted musketeer has thrown his cloak on the table (he couldn't put it on in the midst of a duel).

The right order is B, D, A, C.

Game 5

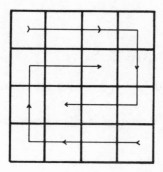

A	C	E	G
L	N	P	I
J	O	M	K
H	F	D	B

The letters are still in alphabetical order, but simultaneously so, on two symmetrical paths as shown by the arrows.

Game 6

NEEDLESS: two pairs of doubled letters.

Game 7

SUE: The names of each pair contain each of the five vowels once.

Game 8

Each wig has a different number of crossings of strands of hair from one through six.

Game 9

WIGGLE: two A's, B's, C's, D's, E's, F's, G's.

Game 10

A brother is present (without his wife but with his son), and his sister (without her husband but with her daughter).

Game 11

Since the word contains no E or G (as in LEG), the only good letter in ERG is R. Then the good letter of SIR is R, which is the third letter of the desired word. I and L are not in the desired word, so the good letter of AIL is A. The A is not the first letter of the desired word, so it must be the second. The good letter of SIC is C, which must begin the desired word: CAR.

Game 12

512: hexagons with bars yield the square of the preceding number; hexagons with a circle yield half of the preceding number.

Game 13

The intruder (bottom right) is drawn in three strokes of the pen instead of four.

Game 14

There are five colors. The first five ties might be all different colors, but the first six cannot be.

Game 15

HARASS: second, fourth, and sixth letters of each word become first, third, and fifth of the next.

Game 16

Let us call the four drawings:

A   B
C   D

C precedes A, where the tire of the left back wheel of the truck has lost its air.

D precedes B, where the policeman has written more in his notebook.

A precedes D, where the small cloud has been pushed by the wind (the flag shows its direction).

The right order is C, A, D, B.

Game 17

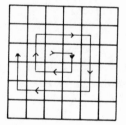

Starting from the center, ABC, ABC, ABC, and so on, has been written along a spiral (arrows).

Game 18

REAPPEARANCE: six vowels and six consonants.

Game 19

Bet on tails. As the coin falls on the table, slap your hand flat on it, saying, "I'd rather see what's underneath so I'll know what didn't come up." You turn the coin over, exposing heads and winning.

But be careful. Your opponent is likely to have two coins, a crooked one for play and a normal one for inspection. If he suspects anything, he may switch them.

Game 20

Each door has a different number of vertical lines in its decoration, from one through seven.

Game 21

SATIATE: begin with first three letters of SUNDAY, MONDAY, TUESDAY, WEDNESDAY, THURSDAY, FRIDAY, SATURDAY.

Game 22

The eight letters of EGIS and LOAM are all different; the four letters of the desired word are among them. Then in PLUG, L and G are the good letters, and in ANEW, A and E are the good letters.

The first letters of the four given words include the A, E, and L, so G must be the first letter of the desired word. The third letters of the given words include A and E, so L is the third letter of the desired word. GELA is not a "common English word," so the answer is GALE.

Game 23

The second house from the bottom on the right has ten visible windows instead of nine.

Game 24

11: each number is the sum of the digits in the number or numbers linked to it from above.

Game 25

The top upright car facing left does not have its front wheels turned.

Game 26

The boat. In the water the coin displaces its *volume* of water; in the boat it displaces its *weight* of water. Since coin metal is heavier than water, the coin weighs more than its corresponding volume of water does.

Game 27

DUCAL: vowels alternate with consonants, but successive words begin with a consonant, a vowel, a consonant . . .

Game 28

Let us call the four drawings:

A   B
C   D

The progressive accumulation of hair on the cloth and on the floor leaves only one possible solution:

Timothy wears a wig, and the right order is B, A, D, C.

B: Timothy has just sat down.

A: The hairdresser has taken Timothy's wig off and cut a little of his hair.

D: The haircut is almost over.

C: Timothy has his wig on again and is ready to leave.

Game 29

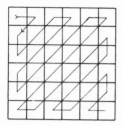

A	A	C	A	E	A
B	B	B	D	B	E
A	C	C	C	D	F
D	B	D	C	G	E
A	E	B	A	D	F
F	A	B	C	G	H

The square is filled, diagonal after diagonal, beginning at the upper left corner (arrows), with the series A, AB, ABC, ABCD, ABCDE, ABCDEF, ABCDEFG, ABCDEFGH.

Game 30

ASHORE: made up of two shorter words, like ACRE, AGE.

Game 31

Yes, it is. Suppose the three friends have run thirty times with these results:
- for the first ten days the order of finish is Timothy, Urban, Vincent.
  - for the next ten days it's Urban, Vincent, Timothy.
  - for the last ten days it's Vincent, Timothy, Urban.

Timothy finished before Urban twenty days out of thirty.
Urban finished before Vincent twenty days out of thirty.
Vincent finished before Timothy twenty days out of thirty.

Game 32

The numbers from 1 through 6 actually appear on each head, disguised as part of the face.

Game 33

ARTERIAL: the two central letters of each word become the first and last letters of the next.

Game 34

Since GUSTO and LIGHT have no good letters, the only good letter in BUILT is B, which begins the desired word. One good letter in BUGLE is B and the other is E (out of place).

The good letters in ADULT are A and D, so the good letter in DYING is D. Y is false, like S, T, and O, so the only good letter in STORY is R, at the correct place. The desired word has the form B . DR . or B . . RD and has to be BEDRA, BEARD, or BAERD. Therefore, it's BEARD.

Game 35

The last fact given means that no one married his son and daughter to the daughter and son of the same friend.

Let us call the five friends by their initials.

"Daughter-in-law of the father of A's son-in-law" means A's daughter. "Son-in-law of the father of C's daughter-in-law" means C's son. Then A's daughter is the sister-in-law of B's son, which can only mean that her brother (A's son) married B's daughter. Similarly, C married his daughter to D's son.

Who is the husband of D's daughter? He cannot be C's or A's son. Let us suppose he is B's son. Then C's daughter's mother-in-law is Mrs. D, while A's son's mother-in-law is Mrs. B. So D's daughter can't have married B's son.

It follows that D's daughter married E's son. D's daughter and B's son have a common mother-in-law: Mrs. E.

Eugene's daughter is married to Bernard's son.

Game 36

24: the number in the center of each circle is the sum of the three numbers on the circumference of the circle.

Game 37

Dickinson is the only one who knows only one of the others. His first name must be Dave.

Bob is neither Dickinson nor Brown. Not knowing Brown, he cannot be Adams nor Carter, so Bob is Emerson.

The first names of the friends at lunch are Alex, Chip, and Elmer. Alex knows Chip and Elmer. Knowing only two friends, he does not know Bob Emerson or Dave Dickinson.

Bob Emerson knows three friends. They are Chip, Dave Dickinson, and Elmer.

Dave Dickinson, knowing only one friend, does not know Chip or Elmer.

Alex and Brown are the only ones to know only two friends. They are the same person: Alex Brown.

Adams's first name is Elmer and Carter's is Chip.

The full names are Elmer Adams, Alex Brown, Chip Carter, Dave Dickinson, and Bob Emerson.

Game 38

The water level remains constant throughout the experiment.

When the ice cube is in the glass, thus floating with the man and the buoy on the water, it displaces its weight of water.

When it falls in the pool it floats again, and still displaces its weight of water.

When it melts it displaces its volume of water. Since it is ice, the volume of water corresponding to its weight is equal to its volume.

Game 39

TENDERNESS: words that sound as if they begin with TWO, FOUR, SIX, EIGHT, TEN.

Game 40

We know that:
- Andrew's house is Belle.
- Bernard's house is Donna.
- Claude's house is Anne.

Their daughters are not so named. Claude cannot be Donna's father and Eugene cannot be Eve's father.

Belle's father, who named his villa Eve, can only be Donald or Eugene.

Similarly, Eve's father is Donald or Eugene. Since he phoned to the last one, he is Donald. His house is Cecilia.

Eugene is Belle's father, Andrew is Donna's father, Bernard is Anne's father, and Claude is Cecilia's father.

Game 41

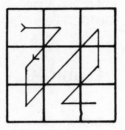

The arrows show how the numbers increase on successive diagonals.

$$1 + 1 = 2$$
$$1 + 2 = 3$$
$$2 + 3 = 5$$
$$3 + 5 = 8$$
$$5 + 8 = 13$$
$$8 + 13 = 21$$

The number in each square is the sum of the numbers in the two preceding squares—a Fibonacci series. The last square contains $13 + 21 = 34$.

Game 42

HIJACKER: three consecutive letters in alphabetical order.

Game 43

Each group of twenty-one persons speaking a language has four subgroups: (1) three languages, (2) two languages, (3) another two-language subgroup (for example, English and German as opposed to French and German in the German group), and (4) one language. There are only three ways of equating twenty-one with four numbers that are all different and all greater than 2:

$$21 = 3 + 4 + 6 + 8$$
$$= 3 + 5 + 6 + 7$$
$$= 3 + 4 + 5 + 9$$

The last line contains the largest of the subgroups, who speak only French (9); so the last line is the French-speaking group.

The number of those who speak English and German but not French must appear as a subgroup on both of the first two lines, that is, as 3 or 6. But this is also true of the subgroup speaking all three languages; this latter must be 3, since 6 does not appear on the last line. So there are six conferees who speak English and German but not French.

Game 44

Each vase has a different number of crossings of lines at right angles, rising by twos from two through fourteen.

Game 45

GENEROUS: two vowels and S, preceded by zero, one, two, three, four, five, letters.

Game 46

We can reorder and restate the statements as follows:
1. If a strategist is a good tactician, he is never vanquished.
2. If a strategist is audacious, he has the confidence of his troops.
3. If a strategist has the confidence of his troops, he is a good tactician. (If he were bad, he would not have their confidence.)
4. If a strategist is never vanquished, he is not despised by women.

Therefore, if a strategist is audacious, he is not despised by women.

Game 47

From Mrs. D's second assertion we know that A is the stepfather of X (who remains to be identified), who is the stepfather of B.

From her first assertion: D is the stepfather of Y, who is the stepfather of Z, who is the stepfather of E.

From her third assertion: C is the stepfather of R, who is the stepfather of S, who is the stepfather of T, who is the stepfather of F.

We know that Mrs. D is not C's mother, for she is speaking to her. There is only one solution that fits these facts: A is the stepfather of D, who is the stepfather of B, who is the stepfather of F, who is the stepfather of E, who is the stepfather of C, who is the stepfather of A.

Game 48

8: each knot yields (below it) the sum of the two horizontal numbers minus the number above the knot.

Game 49

We know that Deer missed a roe and killed a hare. Since Roe did not miss a roe (same name), he did not kill a deer. Likewise, the deer cannot have been killed by Deer or missed by Roe.

Since Hare did not miss a hare or a roe, the doe was not killed by Hare or by Roe, or by Doe. Hence the doe was not missed by Hare.

Only Boar can have killed a doe. Then Hare missed a boar and Roe missed a doe. The deer was killed by Doe and the roe by Hare.

Game 50

The younger son plays one game every two days.

Game 51

INCEST: number of letters in each word is the number in the alphabet of the first letter of the next word. The first word has twenty-six letters, so the second word begins with Z, the twenty-sixth letter in the alphabet, and so on.

Game 52

Let us call the four drawings:

$$
\begin{array}{cc}
A & B \\
C & D
\end{array}
$$

C precedes B, which shows a new stain on the right leg.

D precedes A, which shows a new stain on the chin and cheek.

A precedes C, which shows a new stain on the chest.

The right order is D, A, C, B.

(The state of the motorcycle parts is inconclusive, for a motorcycle can be taken apart as well as put together.)

Game 53

Each number is the sum of three numbers:
- above.
- above left.
- left.

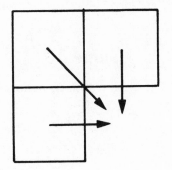

The missing number is 63.

Game 54

GERMANE: change one letter in each word to get a country (CHINA, FRANCE, SPAIN, CHILE, CUBA, PERU, GERMANY).

Game 55

Three shoes have low heels and laces, and three have high heels and no laces. The seventh has a high heel and laces.

Game 56

KID: begin with A, end with B, begin with C, end with D...

Game 57

We can reorder and restate Timothy's opinions as follows:

6. If the hotel accepts dogs, its prices are high.
3. If prices are high, the food is good.
1. If the food is good, the waitresses are courteous.
5. If the waitresses are courteous, the hotel is open all year long.
2. If a hotel is open all year long, it has a view of the ocean.
7. If there is a view of the ocean, there is a swimming pool.
4. If there is a swimming pool, there is honeysuckle on the walls.

Therefore, hotels that accept dogs have honeysuckle on the walls.

Game 58

Six clocks have their hands in correct positions, but the hour hand of the seventh clock shows about "ten of" while the minute hand shows "ten after."

Game 59

10: numbers increase by 1 if they go down vertically and by 2 if they go down diagonally.

Game 60

Lebrun is taller than the warehouseman, so he is not the warehouseman or the salesman. He is the accountant.

The salesman is not Lebrun and not Lenoir (a married man). He is Leblanc.

By elimination, Lenoir is the warehouseman.

Game 61

PAROCHIALISM: one, two, three, four, five, six, seven consonants.

Game 62

Imagine the square is cut onto four squares. Their diagonals have opposite symbols:

- plus—minus;
- black circle—white circle;
- black square—white square, etc.

The missing symbol is a downward-pointing arrow.

Game 63

ABSTEMIOUS: each of the five vowels appears once.

Game 64

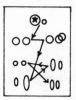

Each cycle has the front wheel's tire valve in a different position, rotating forward by about an eighth of a turn per drawing.

Game 65

STENOGRAPHIC: no letter appears twice.

Game 66

Assigning Smith the bottom seat, the four men can only sit this way:

SMYTHE

PSMITH   SMYTH

SMITH

Hence Smyth is the grocer, Psmith is the tobacconist, and Smythe is the baker.

Game 67

No. He says that if there is a front-wheel drive, the car has a good hold on the road; if so, it is heavy; if so, it has good brakes; if so, it is powerful; and if so, it is high-priced.

Game 68

7: The number under each circle is the sum of the number or numbers above that are linked to the circle, divided by the number of dots inside the circle.

Game 69

The man at top left wears eight visible pieces of cloth instead of seven.

Game 70

Note that the three correct answers need not all be different.

Can the first answer be Polk? If so, only #1 answered the question correctly. Then #3 and #4 must each be right on one of the last two questions, where the answers must be either Fillmore or Polk. But #5 must be right on one of these questions too, although he answered Taylor to both. This is impossible, so the first answer is not Polk.

Can the first answer be Fillmore? If so, by similar reasoning on the answers of #1 and #2, the last two answers must be either Polk or Taylor; but #6 answered Fillmore to both. Still another impossibility.

By elimination, the correct first answer is Taylor. Then the second answer is Fillmore and the third is Taylor again.

Game 71

Let us tabulate the descriptions:

	Eyes	*Size*	*Coat*	*Hat*
Guard	blue	tall	vest	yes
Cashier	dark	short	vest	yes
Secretary	green	medium	raincoat	yes
Director	gray	tall	vest	no

Not more than one witness can be right about any detail, or there would have to be another detail that no witness is right about. Therefore, the criminal did not wear a hat. The director was right about that and thus wrong about everything else, so the criminal had no vest, was not tall and did not have gray eyes. The only detail the guard can have right is the blue eyes. The correct detail of the cashier is that the robber was short; that of the secretary is that he wore a raincoat.

The criminal was blue-eyed and short, wearing a raincoat and bareheaded.

Game 72

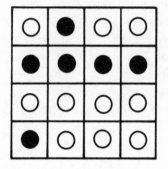

In each successive 2 × 2 square, top left, top right, bottom left, bottom right, there is one more white circle.

Game 73

The three inhabitants can't be all from the plain or all from the mountains, or all the answers would be the same.

Can there be two from the mountains and one from the plain? No, for they would all answer yes to the second question.

Therefore there are two from the plain and one from the mountains. They all say no to the first question. At the second question, those from the plain say no and the one from the mountains says yes.

Then "Grb" means no.

Game 74

REST: contains three consonants, which are consecutive consonants in the alphabet.

Game 75

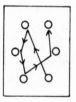

Looked at closely, every seat shows a roman number, from I through VI.

Game 76

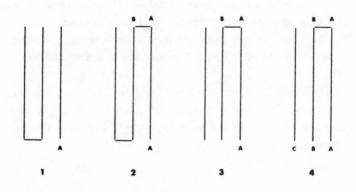

In the basement Timothy fastens any two of the three wires together. He labels the free wire A.

In the attic, Timothy tests every pair of wires with the meter—that is, three possible pairings. The pair the current goes through is the one fastened in the basement. The leftover wire is A's other end and must be labeled A too. Timothy then fastens A to a randomly chosen wire of the pair, which he labels B. The third wire is labeled C.

Back in the basement, Timothy unfastens the two wires and tests all three possible parts of wires with the meter. The pair with current is fastened in the attic, and the wire not labeled A must be labeled B. The third is labeled C.

Game 77

Elizabeth's husband is not Henry. He cannot be Roger or Peter, who are not dancing, so Elizabeth is married to Louis.

Likewise, Henry's wife is not Elizabeth, or Anne, or Mary. Henry is married to Jeanne.

Peter's wife is Mary.

Roger's wife is Anne.

Game 78

62: each circle (except the corner ones) is the target of two arrows, one long and one short. The number in each circle is the number the short arrow comes from plus twice the number the long arrow comes from.

Game 79

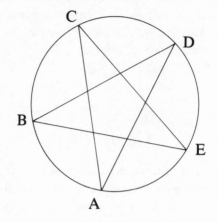

Since no one is elected, "his" refers to the same person as "everyone" in the last paragraph.

Let us consider Anthony's case. He can't vote for himself: he would vote for his left neighbor too.

Anthony can't vote for Bernard, because Bernard is Anthony's left neighbor and that would mean Anthony has to vote for himself too, which is contradictory.

Anthony can't vote for Claude: Claude would have to vote for Anthony's left neighbor Bernard, Bernard for David, David for Claude, and Claude for Edwin, which is contradictory.

Anthony can't vote for Edwin. Edwin would vote for Bernard, Bernard for Anthony, and Anthony for Claude, which is contradictory.

Anthony can only vote for David, who votes for Bernard, who votes for Edwin, who votes for Claude, who votes for Anthony.

Game 80

INCOMMUNICABILITY: none of these long words contains an E.

Game 81

Three locks and three keys are enough. Let the keys be A, B, and C. The first associate gets keys A and B; the second associate keys B and C; and the third associate keys C and A.

Now each associate has only two keys out of three. He cannot open the door alone, but can with the help of either other associate.

Game 82

From the second statement, philosophers are mortals (or they would be ignorant of philosophy).

Since all mortals are poets, philosophers are poets.

Since no poet practices mathematics, no philosopher does either.

Then a mathematician cannot be a philosopher. The four assertions are inconsistent.

Game 83

△   △ ✚   △ ✚ ▽   △ ✚ ▽ ✖   •••

Reading horizontally from left to right, line by line, there is a series of one symbol, then two, three, and so on. Once the *n*th symbol in a series is established it does not change. The missing symbol, being fourth in such a series, is **X**.

Game 84

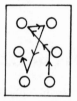

Each phone cord makes a different number of loops, from one through six.

Game 85

LOW: letters of each word are in alphabetical order.

Game 86

17: to the right of each horizontal T is the product of the two numbers at the left plus 2.

Game 87

Three portraits have a beard in a rectangular frame, and three have no beard in an oval frame. The portrait at bottom right has no beard in a rectangular frame.

Game 88

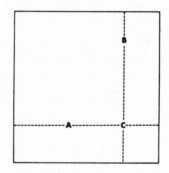

Let A be the first cook and B the second.

If A and B are in the same row, A is taller.

Likewise, if A and B are in the same column, B is shorter.

If they are in different columns and rows, let C be the volunteer in A's row and B's column. C is shorter than A, but taller than B.

So A is always taller than B.

Game 89

MAROON: begin with first three letters of JANUARY, FEBRUARY, MARCH.

Game 90

It is simpler to consider which keys are *not* given to whom.

The director gets the keys to all the locks and need not be considered further.

Let A, B, C, D, and E be the assistant director and the four department heads.

A gets all the keys but one, and B, C, D, and E all get the key A doesn't get. Now only the remaining keys of B, C, D, and E need be considered.

Each group of two department heads should lack one key. There are six such groups, so seven keys are needed.

Here is the distribution of keys:

X	A	B	C	D	E
1		1	1	1	1
2	2			2	2
3	3		3		3
4	4		4	4	
5	5	5			5
6	6	6		6	
7	7	7	7		

Game 91

Violence is accompanied by incompetence, which excludes wisdom, without which there is no knowledge and, therefore, no hope.

Game 92

ANNALS: doubled consonant between identical vowels.

Game 93

On each label a small part is folded or torn. Its position turns clockwise from bottle to bottle.

Game 94

Al mentions his own boat, so it is true that "Susie-Q" and "Seagull" have radios. Also they don't belong to him.

"Seagull" can't belong to Claude, or his sentence would be true, and he couldn't say the boat belongs to Al.

Likewise, Dick can't own "Seagull" or "Mary Jean." Bert owns "Seagull."

"Seagull" has a radio. Then Bert's sentence is true, for, like Al, he mentions three boats with a radio; so Claude does have a radio. Since Claude can't own Al's boat or "Seagull," he owns "Susie-Q."

"The Big One" belongs to Dick and "Mary Jean" to Al.

Game 95

19: the number in each square is the product of the numbers in the northeast and northwest squares minus the number in the north square.

Game 96

A robot's head, hands, and feet can each be shaped like a human being's or not. Six robots have two human elements (head, hands; or head, feet; or hands, feet). The middle robot at the right has only a human-shaped head.

Game 97

Twenty locks are needed. The director owns all the keys. Each assistant director should lack five keys, one in common with each department head. (The two sets of five keys should not overlap.) Each group of three department heads should lack one key. There are ten such groups, so $10 + 5 + 5 = 20$ keys are distributed.

Here are the keys that are *not* given to assistant directors A and B and to department heads C, D, E, F, and G:

A	B	C	D	E	F	G
1		1				
2			2			
3				3		
4					4	
5						5
	6	6				
	7		7			
	8			8		
	9				9	
	10					10
		11	11	11		
		12		12	12	
		13			13	13
		14	14		14	
		15	15			15
		16		16		16
			17	17	17	
			18		18	18
			19	19		19
				20	20	20

Game 98

The matrix shows what the child will answer (truthfully on lines 2, 4, 6, 8; falsely on lines 1, 3, 5, 7), for all eight residence possibilities:

Village of man	Village of woman	Village of child	First answer	Second answer
big	big	big	yes	yes
big	big	small	no	no
big	small	big	no	yes
big	small	small	yes	no
small	big	big	yes	no
small	big	small	no	no
small	small	big	yes	no
small	small	small	no	no

Only lines 1, 2, 6, and 8, where the first and second answers are identical, can actually occur. In each of these four cases, the village of the man is not bigger than the village of the woman. So the correct first answer is no.

In the same four cases, the village of the child is not bigger than the village of the man. So the correct second answer is also no. (This does not mean, however, that the child said no. In the case of line 1, he said yes; in the other three cases he said no.)

Game 99

A's statement must be true: if he is lying, he is last and he is also first or second, which is contradictory. So A is third or fourth.

If D is telling the truth, E is lying and D is first and is lying, which is contradictory. So E is not second, and D is first or second.

If E is lying, D is first and E second. But D is lying when he says E is second. Therefore, E is telling the truth, which makes him third, fourth, or fifth. D is not first, but second.

Only B or C can be first. If B is not first, since he is also not second he is telling the truth, and C is third, and cannot be first either, which is impossible. Then B is first and C is not third.

C, being neither first nor second, is telling the truth that A is behind E. E is third, A is fourth, and C is fifth.

The athletes placed in this order: B, D, E, A, C.

Game 100

The person riding Bernard's bicycle and wearing Claude's hat can't be Bernard or Claude: he is Andrew.

If Bernard is riding Andrew's bicycle, Claude is riding his own. He is not, so Bernard is riding Claude's bicycle and Claude is riding Andrew's.

About the Author

Born in Tours, France, Pierre Berloquin was trained as an operations research engineer, which gave him an excellent background in mathematics and logical thinking. His popular column on "Games and Paradoxes" appears twice monthly in *The World of Science*, a supplement of the Paris newspaper, *Le Monde*.

Booey the Poltergeist

The mischievous ghost who haunts Cacklefur Castle.

Boneham

The butler to the von Cacklefur family, and a snob right down to the tips of his whiskers.

Baby

He was adopted and raised with love by the von Cacklefurs.

Chef Stewrat

The cook at Cacklefur Castle. He dreams of creating the ultimate stew.

Boris von Cacklefur

Creepella's father, and the funeral director at Fabumouse Funerals.

Madame LaTomb

The family housekeeper. A ferocious were-canary nests in her hair.

Chompers

The von Cacklefur family's meat-eating guard plant.

Geronimo Stilton

CREEPELLA VON CACKLEFUR
MEET ME IN HORRORWOOD

Scholastic Inc.

New York   Toronto   London   Auckland

Sydney   Mexico City   New Delhi   Hong Kong

If you purchased this book without a cover, you should be aware that this book is stolen property. It was reported as "unsold and destroyed" to the publisher, and neither the author nor the publisher has received any payment for this "stripped book."

No part of this book may be reproduced, stored in a retrieval system, or transmitted in any form or by any means, electronic, mechanical, photocopying, recording, or otherwise, without written permission of the copyright holder. For information regarding permission, please contact: Atlantyca S.p.A., Via Leopardi 8, 20123 Milan, Italy; e-mail foreignrights@atlantyca.it, www.atlantyca.com.

ISBN 978-0-545-30743-7

Copyright © 2010 by Edizioni Piemme S.p.A., Via Tiziano 32, 20145 Milan, Italy.

International Rights © Atlantyca S.p.A.

English translation © 2011 by Atlantyca S.p.A.

GERONIMO STILTON names, characters, and related indicia are copyright, trademark, and exclusive license of Atlantyca S.p.A. All rights reserved. The moral right of the author has been asserted.

Based on an original idea by Elisabetta Dami.

www.geronimostilton.com

Published by Scholastic Inc., 557 Broadway, New York, NY 10012.

SCHOLASTIC and associated logos are trademarks and/or registered trademarks of Scholastic Inc.

Stilton is the name of a famous English cheese. It is a registered trademark of the Stilton Cheese Makers' Association. For more information, go to www.stiltoncheese.com.

Text by Geronimo Stilton
Original title *Mistero a Castelteschio*
Cover by Giuseppe Ferrario
Illustrations by Ivan Bigarella (pencils and inks) and
Giorgio Campioni (color)
Map of Cacklefur Castle: Color by Christian Aliprandi
Graphics by Yuko Egusa

Special thanks to Tracey West
Translated by Lidia Tramontozzi
Interior design by Elizabeth Frances Herzog

12 11 10 9 8 7 6 5 4   12 13 14 15 15 16/0

Printed in the U.S.A.   40
First printing, August 2011

A SHADOW IN
THE NIGHT . . .

It was almost midnight. I was working late in my office at *The Rodent's Gazette*, the most famous newspaper in New Mouse City. Suddenly, I thought I saw the **SHADOW** of a bat outside my window.

WEIRD!

Could it really be a bat? I looked out of the window. A **FULL** moon shone brightly in the black sky. But I didn't see any bats.

Oh, I'm sorry! I forgot to introduce myself. My name is Stilton, *Geronimo Stilton*. I'm the editor of *The Rodent's Gazette.* I turned back to my computer, but I felt strange, as if somebody was staring at me. **WEIRD!**

I headed to the office kitchen. A nice **CUP** of hot cheddar tea was just what I needed to calm down.

A shiver ran down my back, curling my whiskers. I couldn't shake that creepy feeling. So I turned off the light and headed home.

As I walked, I had the **ODD** feeling that someone was following me. I walked faster and faster. Finally, I reached the front door of my house. I *quickly* went inside and locked the door behind me. Then I breathed a sigh of relief.

I was just putting on my apron when a **chilly** breeze hit my whiskers. The window was wide open. **WEIRD!** I was sure I had closed it that morning. As I moved to shut it, I thought I heard the rustling of wings outside.

Zoom! Something zipped right past me! I felt it brush against my **whiskers**. Then something heavy landed right on my tail! I let out a bloodcurdling scream:

SQUEAK!

A large package wrapped in purple paper bounced off of my tail and landed on the floor. Then a tiny voice yelled in my ear:

"Message for you! Message for you! Message for you!"

I recognized that voice. It was **Bitewing**, Creepella von Cacklefur's pet bat!

I rubbed my bruised tail.

"Open the box! It's for you!" the purple bat screeched.

I tore off the purple paper and opened the box. The first thing I saw was a card shaped like a **TOMBSTONE**! There were two hearts on the front of the tombstone, with the initials *G* and *B* underneath. **WEIRD!**

Underneath the tombstone were a computer disc and a letter written on purple paper.

The label on the disc said *Meet Me in Horrorwood*. The letter read:

To my little cheese nip, Geronimo,

I'm sending you a new adventure (on the disc!). You must publish it immediately! It's a scary love story!

Inside this purple box, you will also find a tombstone-shaped wedding invitation. If you want to find out who's getting married at Cacklefur Castle, read the story!

I was so curious, I began to read it right away. . . .

CVC

MEET ME IN HORRORWOOD

★ STORY AND ILLUSTRATIONS BY CREEPELLA VON CACKLEFUR ★

To my little cheese nip,

...m sending you a new adven...

...isc!). You must publish it immediately.

...a scary love story!

Inside this purple box, you will also find a

...tombstone-shaped wedding invitation. If you

...ant to find out who's getting married at

...tle, read the story!

THERE'S SOMETHING WRONG . . .

"Auntie?"

Creepella von Cacklefur slowly opened her eyes. Someone was **tugging** on her blanket.

"Auntie, wake up! We've got a **problem**!"

Creepella propped herself up on her pillows and **YAWNED**. Her niece, Shivereen, was standing by the bed next to her. She looked very worried.

Kafka, the von Cacklefur family's pet cockroach, slept at the foot of Creepella's bed. He slowly opened his beady eyes. Then he wiggled his antennae to greet Shivereen.

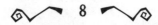

Creepella saw the first rays of the sun rising in the GLOOMY sky. Cacklefur Castle was as quiet as a tomb.

She felt very sleepy. Last night, a magnificent full moon shone in the sky. It had inspired her to write an article about **werewolves** for *The Shivery News*. Being published in the most famous newspaper in Mysterious Valley was a great achievement. Creepella had worked late into the night, and now she didn't feel like waking up. But Shivereen looked like she had something important to say.

"What's wrong?" Creepella asked, yawning again.

"There's something wrong with Gorgo!" Shivereen cried. "He's not stinking like he always does. His GREEN SLIME coloring has faded. And he won't eat!"

GORGO

Cacklefur Castle's moat monster

BIRTHPLACE: A stinky swamp that's impossible to find

AGE: Between 15 and 150 monster years

SIZE: Always changing

FAVORITE FOOD: Eats everything, but prefers rotten food with vintage rust

FAVORITE COLOR: Slime green

FAVORITE PERFUME: Essence of Smelly Socks

FAVORITE BOOK: *Green Eggs and Hammers*

IDENTIFYING MARKS: Green boils all over his body

It appears there may be only one other creature of this type in the entire world — a female monster.

Creepella jumped out of bed, alarmed. "What? Gorgo isn't hungry?" she shrieked. "THAT'S IMPOSSIBLE! He's got a bottomless pit for a stomach!"

She quickly dressed and rushed out of her room in a frenzy. Boneham, the butler, was waiting for her at the door.

See? He won't eat!

"Miss Creepella, the situation is serious," he said. "Please FOLLOW ME!"

They quickly reached the moat, where the monster lived. Boneham threw a rusty old bicycle into the muddy water. Bicycles were one of Gorgo's favorite foods.

"Bluuuuuuuuurp!"

Gorgo let out a lonely cry. He didn't even look at the bicycle.

Bluuuuurp!

"See? He hasn't eaten anything since yesterday," Boneham said sadly. "All he does is cry out with heartbreaking bluvvvvvvvRps!"

Creepella shook her head, worried. "I've never seen him like this," she agreed. "Did you try throwing him an old, DISGUSTING, smelly shoe?"

Boneham nodded. "I did. He didn't even notice it. It's still floating down there!"

"This is serious," Creepella said. "What if we try a box of delicious RUSTY nails?"

"I already did," the butler replied. "He didn't touch one!"

Creepella frowned. "This is *very* serious. How about a nice bag of ROTTEN garbage? I'm sure he could never resist that!"

14

The butler sighed. "No. He wouldn't even taste it!"

"This is **very, very, very** serious," Creepella said thoughtfully. "There's only one solution."

"You're not thinking —"

"I am!" Creepella cried. "We need a family reunion!"

The butler turned P△LE. "Please think this through, Miss Creepella," he said. "Remember the last reunion? It was so **LIVELY**, we had to rebuild an entire wing of the castle!"

Creepella's green eyes sparkled. "That was a FUN party! But there won't be any fun this time. We have a very serious problem to solve. Gorgo is SICK!"

FAMILY
REUNION

The butler ran up the **STAIRS** to the top of the tallest tower in Cacklefur Castle, **Bitewing's tower**. Grandpa Frankenstein's inventions were piled high in the small room. He created them all when he was a young mouse learning his trade at the Weird Wizard Shop.

Boneham went into the gloomy room and walked over to a large **MACHINE** covered by a heavy cloth. He pulled the **MOLDY** cloth aside to reveal a strange contraption, the **Cacklefur Emergency Alarm**. Everyone in the von Cacklefur family knew

the HIDEOUS sound it made, and they always came running when they heard it.

Boneham turned the crank, and a DEAFENING sound echoed through all of Mysterious Valley.

ALARM!

ALARM!

ALARM!

One by one, each member of the von Cacklefur family gathered in the BANQUET HALL.

"Welcome!" Creepella told the group. Her voice was serious. "I have assembled you here because we have a problem."

"Gorgo is sick!" Shivereen exclaimed.

Creepella

Madame LaTomb

Booey

Grand
Cryp

Baby

The family members exchanged worried and confused glances.

"Sick? What are his **symptoms**?" asked Madame LaTomb, the family housekeeper.

"His color is sickly . . . it's not as bright as his usual **SLIME GREEN**," Creepella began.

Boris von Cacklefur

Grandpa Frankenstein

Shivereen

Snip and Snap

Chef Stewrat

Kafka

Chompers

"Well, it's delightfully FOGGY outside," said Creepella's father, Boris von Cacklefur. "It's normal to have pale coloring in this weather."

"Maybe, but there's something else," Creepella went on. "He makes a very sad noise. It's an odd 'bluvvvvvĭp' that brings TEARS to my eyes."

Howler, the were-canary, peeked out of Madame LaTomb's puffy hair.

"Bah! So much worry about nothing!" the man-eating bird chirped. "He's probably just got an upset stomach."

"Impossible!" Shivereen told him. "He's eaten nothing since yesterday!"

"Good gravy!" exclaimed Chef Stewrat. "Not even my stew?"

Creepella shook her head.

The banquet hall got very quiet. Everyone was very worried about Gorgo.

Then a **LOUD** voice rang out. "Hmm. Pale color . . . a **sad** cry . . . no appetite . . . but of course! The symptoms are clear!"

The voice belonged to Grandma Crypt. She jumped up on her chair.

"I know what's the matter with Gorgo!"

Every creature in the hall looked at her — even **KAFKA**, the pet cockroach, and **CHOMPERS**, the meat-eating plant.

"It's just like the main character of the last book I read, *Without You My Heart Molds*, written by Billy Squeakspeare," Grandma Crypt announced. "Gorgo is in **love**!"

"Gorgo is in love?" everyone asked at once. "In love with whom?"

Grandma Crypt shrugged. "I have no idea."

"**We do! We do!**" chanted Snip and Snap, the troublemaking twins. "If we tell you, can we get a second serving of stew cake?"

Creepella scowled at her nephews. "Cake? Gorgo is SICK and the only thing you can think of is cake? You'd better tell us what you know right now!"

Snip took a **POSTCARD** from Snap's pocket and handed it to Creepella.

"Here, we found it on the bank of the moat," Snip said.

BLOBBINA

Female monster and Horrorwood film actress

EDUCATION: Swamp School of Drama

AGE: A lady never reveals her age!

SIZE: Big, but perfect for a slime monster

FAVORITE FOOD: Wilted flowers

FAVORITE COLOR: Pale pink

FAVORITE PERFUME: Moldy Violets

FAVORITE BOOK: *Heart of Mud* by Billy Squeakspeare

IDENTIFYING MARKS: A dark purple mole by her mouth

It appears there may be only one other creature of this type in the entire world — a male monster.

"Gorgo really is in love!" Boris von Cacklefur exclaimed happily.

"And she's a **MOVIE STAR**!" added Grandpa Frankenstein.

Madame LaTomb sighed. "It's so romantic. As a young girl, I, too, was in love with a famouse movie star. **Humphrey Bograt** was so handsome!"

The crabby canary snorted. "**LOVE!** What a waste of time."

"Look who's talking," Creepella said, **POINTING** at Howler's beak. "Did you forget how you fell head over wings for that saucy parakeet last year?"

The canary blushed and dove into the thickest part of Madame LaTomb's hair.

Booey the ghost had a faraway look on his see-through face. "One can never forget

love," he said. "It's almost better than an old **RUINED** castle."

"Yes, better than a velvet-covered CASKET," added Boris.

"Or a great big pot of ten-year-old *STEW*," Chef Stewrat said dreamily.

Creepella turned to Grandpa Frankenstein. "What about you, Grandfather?" she asked him. "Have you ever been **LOVESICK** like Gorgo?"

"Yes, my dear," he replied. "Once, a lovely MUMMY broke my heart. But then I met Grandma Crypt, and the rest is history."

The entire hall filled with deep sighs.

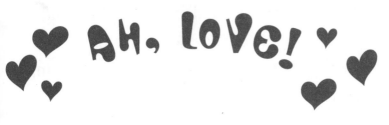

A Love Letter

Everyone started talking at once. They all wanted to help Gorgo win the **love** of his dreams.

Grandma Crypt was the family's best expert on love stories and remedies for **broken hearts**. "He needs to write her a nice love **LETTER**," she decided.

"Gorgo is too shy to write to her," Boris pointed out. He looked right at his daughter. "My dear Creepella, can you help him?"

"*I'm on it!*" she replied. "I'm going straight to my room to write the letter."

Creepella sat at her desk, picked up her tarantula paperweight, and took out a sheet of yellowed paper. Then she chose a pencil with a bright Violet tip. Her beetle nibbled on the tip until it was nice and SHARP.

"Now I can begin!" she exclaimed. "Hmm. How does one address a monster movie star?"

"Dear Sliminess . . ." NO.

"TO A MARVELOUS MASS OF MUD . . ." NO, NO

"SMELLIEST LEADING ACTRESS . . ." NO, NO, N

Creepella shook her head. She crumpled up the third piece of wasted paper and threw it in the cauldron-shaped recycling bin.

"I've got it!" she shouted, and she began to write. . . .

...ine of my heart, there is no monster finer,
...y name is Gorgo, your faithful admirer.

I have devoured all of your films, from A to Z . . . .
I even nibbled on the DVDs!

Your eyes are as dark as a stormy night,
You turn my stomach and make my heart take flight.

I live in Cacklefur Castle; you can get here by boat.
We can watch the sun as it sets over the moat.

If you visit I will give everything to you,
Bugs, garbage, and rusted metal, too.

Please, my beloved, answer me.
If you do, you will make me monstrously happy.

Disgustingly yours,

Gorgo

Bitewing flapped his wings.

"Are you done yet?
Are you done yet?
Are you done yet?"

he screeched.

"Yes! I've written a monstrously romantic letter," Creepella replied. She handed him the sheet of paper. "You have to take this to Blobbina at Horrorwood Studios!"

"But the set is **SOOOOO** far," the bat complained. "It's a long, tiring flight."

 Creepella opened a drawer and pulled out a box of **chocolates**.

Bitewing's eyes got wide. He smacked his lips.

"Are those chocolate-covered ants?" he cried. "My favorite!"

"They're all yours!" Creepella told him.

She threw some of the chocolate bugs in the air. Bitewing *SWOOPED* and *SOARED*, quickly catching each one in his mouth. Now he had the energy he needed for the long trip. He gripped the letter between his TEETH and flew out of the window.

Creepella started to work on another newspaper article. When she stopped to look at the clock, she saw that a few hours had passed.

"STRANGE! Bitewing isn't back yet," she said with a frown. "And it's time for his favorite TV show, SO YOU THINK YOU CAN FLY? He never misses that. I must find him!"

A FRIGHTFUL MOVIE SET

Creepella jumped into her super-deluxe hearse and headed for the film studios in Horrorwood.

The famous director Sam Shivers was directing his new **HORROR** movie: a terrifying monster story starring Blobbina. The gossip columns were already saying that her role in *Shrieks and Monsters* could win Blobbina a **GOLDEN CLAW** award for

in a Horror Film.

"Bitewing!" Creepella called out. Then she **muttered** to herself, "Where could he have gone?"

Rodents of all shapes and colors were scurrying around the set. Actors practiced their lines. **Nervous** technicians moved lights and wires. Costume makers **HURRIED** by with armloads of material. Stagehands carried props from place to place.

Suddenly, Creepella heard a deep voice behind her.

"Your eyes are as **BEAUTIFUL** as swamp pearls."

Creepella turned, but she couldn't tell which mouse had spoken. Even so, she batted her lashes.

"Thank you," she replied sweetly. "It must be my **eye shadow** made of ground beetle shell."

"Your hair is as **shiny** as swamp snakes," the mysterious rodent continued.

Creepella giggled. "It must be my shampoo: **SUPER SLUG SLIME**."

She moved toward a huge panel on the set. The voice sounded like it was coming from there.

"And your blond fur is as **bright** as the full moon!" the rodent exclaimed.

Creepella stopped. "Wait. My fur isn't blond!"

She peeked behind the panel and saw that her admirer was actually an actor, practicing his **LINES** for a romantic scene. He looked at her, confused.

"May I help you?" he asked.

"Ah, no . . . I mean, yes!" she said. "Have you seen a little purple **BAT** around here?"

The actor nodded. "I think I saw one in the special effects warehouse next door."

She went to the warehouse and walked inside. It was completely **dark**.

"Crusty cobwebs! I can't see a thing!" Creepella complained. "I'll just turn on this light switch."

Creepella found a lot of things in the warehouse:

a **GHOST** costume,

a pair of werewolf **gloves**,

a set of razor-sharp canine teeth,

and a wild cat mask with tangled whiskers.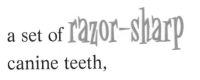

But she couldn't find Bitewing!

"I know what to do," she said. She took a little jar of mosquito jam from her pocket and held it in front of her.

"Tiny little bat of my nightmares where are you?"

she called out.

Soon she heard a fluttering of wings and Bitewing's cry.

"Hiiiiiiiiiiiiiiiiiiiiiiiii!"

"Finally! There you are," Creepella exclaimed. "Did you deliver the letter?"

Bitewing slurped down his delicious snack. "**Yum, yum, yum**," he said happily. "Well . . . I've been **flying** all over the place, but I can't find Blobbina. Nobody seems to know where she is!"

"Hmm," Creepella said thoughtfully. "It seems I have a new MYSTERY on my paws." She briskly walked out of the warehouse. "Follow me," she told Bitewing. "Maybe the director can give us a C L U e !"

A MONSTROUS LEADING LADY

They found Sam Shivers inside his trailer, drinking a glass of SWAMP JUICE. He was staring sadly at a poster of Blobbina on the wall.

Creepella stuck her head through the open doorway. "May I come in?"

Shivers didn't answer. Instead, he sighed and wiped a **TEAR** from his furry cheek with his handkerchief.

Bitewing flew into the trailer and circled the director's head. "*What's wrong? What's wrong? What's wrong?*"

Sam Shivers **LOUDLY** blew his nose into his handkerchief.

Creepella stepped inside. "Mr. Shivers, we're looking for Blobbina."

At the mention of the monster's name, Shivers burst out *crying*. He buried his face on his desk.

"What a disaster!
What a tragedy!
What a calamity!

My directing career is over, done for, ruined!"

Then, very slowly and dramatically, he lifted his head and placed a paw on his forehead.

"I'll have to go work in my aunt's **earthworm** beauty salon!" he exclaimed.

Creepella did not like whiners. "Get ahold

of yourself!" she said sternly. "I'm sure things aren't as **TERRIBLE** as that. Tell me what happened."

The director sniffed noisily. "It's about **BLOBBINA**, my leading lady," he began. "She's . . . she's . . . she's . . ."

"She's *what*?" Creepella and Bitewing asked impatiently.

"SHE'S DISAPPEARED!"

Shivers shouted. Then he started to sob again.

Creepella raised her left eyebrow. "I knew there was a mystery to solve," she said. "Luckily, I know just who can help us."

She took a stash of **BUSINESS CARDS** out of her pocket.

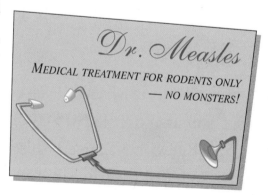

"Let's see now, here's one." She read the card. "plumber Russ T. Sink? No, that's not it."

She looked at another card. "MEDIEVAL PACKAGE DELIVERY? No, that's not it, either!"

She read a third card. "Dr. Measles? Probably not. He doesn't know a thing about monsters."

The director stared at Creepella. How could one mouse have **so many** business cards?

"AHHH! I've got it!" Creepella finally shrieked. "Here it is." She waved the card under the director's snout.

MR. M.
MONSTER EXPERT
Leave all urgent messages at P.O. Bat Box 17

"Who is Mr. M.?" asked Sam Shivers. He sounded a little **suspicious**.

Bitewing flapped his wings furiously. "What do you mean, 'who is he?' He's the

most famouse expert on monsters in Mysterious Valley! **BIG** monsters, SMALL monsters, **Smelly** monsters, SCARY monsters, sweet monsters, SLIMY monsters — he knows them all!"

"He'll know how to help us," Creepella added. She quickly SCRIBBLED a message and gave it to Bitewing.

"Take this to Mr. M.!" she cried.

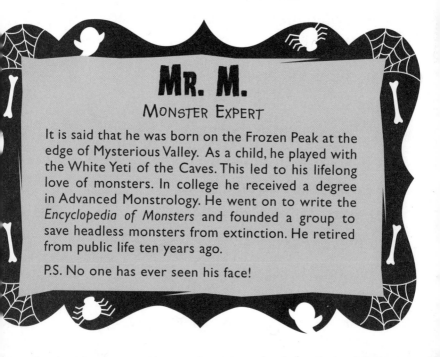

MR. M.
MONSTER EXPERT

It is said that he was born on the Frozen Peak at the edge of Mysterious Valley. As a child, he played with the White Yeti of the Caves. This led to his lifelong love of monsters. In college he received a degree in Advanced Monstrology. He went on to write the *Encyclopedia of Monsters* and founded a group to save headless monsters from extinction. He retired from public life ten years ago.

P.S. No one has ever seen his face!

A Dinner Invitation for Billy

While Creepella searched for Blobbina, Billy Squeakspeare, the famous AUTHOR, was trying to take a nap in his bedroom at Squeakspeare Mansion. When he inherited the mansion, Billy learned he had to sleep during the day because the place was infested with 13 GHOSTS.

Every night at the stroke of midnight, the ghosts would start cleaning the house. This woke Billy up every time, and he could never get back to sleep. But napping during the day wasn't always easy, either. For instance, today someone kept ringing and ringing the doorbell. Billy reluctantly **DRAGGED** himself out of bed. A loud voice was calling out from behind the door.

"Express letter for Mr. Squeakspeare!"

"Wh-who is it?" Billy asked in a sleepy voice. He still had his **nightcap** on his head.

"I'm the messenger from Rattenbaum Mansion," the visitor replied. "I'm looking for the famouse Mr. Billy Squeakspeare!"

Billy opened the door and found himself facing a **BiZARRE** rodent wearing a strange costume. A tall white wig was perched on his head. His red uniform was trimmed in gold, but it was covered in patches, and **MOTHS** were flying out of it.

"Are you the famous Mr. Billy —" began the messenger.

Billy **CUT** him short. "Yes, yes, that's me, but —"

Before he could finish the sentence, the rodent gave him an old, YELLOWED envelope. Then he strutted away with his snout up in the air.

Puzzled, Billy turned the envelope in his hand. His great-great-great-uncle William,

For me?

For the famous Billy Squeakspeare...

the thirteenth GHOST in the mansion, appeared next to him.

"Nephew, is that envelope for me?" he asked.

"Actually, it's for me, from the Rattinbottoms . . . or maybe the Rottendams . . . or the Rittanbams . . ." Billy replied.

William looked excited. "Do you mean the Rattenbaums? They're on my WEDDING list!"

"W-wedding?" Billy stammered. He was a very **NERVOUS** mouse. "Who's getting married?"

"You, of course!" William said in his booming voice. "I jotted down the names of all the single female rodents in Mysterious Valley. There are three in the Rattenbaum household!"

Billy looked TERRIFIED. "Wh-what are you

talking about? I'm too young to get married!"

"'Young'? You've already got COBWEBS on your face," said his great-great-great-uncle. "Now hurry up and open the envelope!"

With a sigh, Billy pulled out the letter.

"You know, I've heard that the Rattenbaum triplets are really delightful," William

---

To the Famous Mr. Billy Squeakspeare,

We are happy to learn that a famous author like yourself has settled in Gloomeria. Since you probably have not found anyone to socialize with in this bad-mannered city, you absolutely must come join us at the very elegant and sophisticated Rattenbaum Mansion for dinner this very evening.

We sincerely hope you will accept this invitation (in fact, we will not take no for an answer).

Our whiskers are twitching in anticipation of your visit.

The Most Noble Rattenbaum Family

assured him. He slapped Billy on the back, but his ghostly paw went right through him. "It would make me so happy if you would settle down and MARRY a nice rodent. That way, you'll give me a little nephew who will grow up in this mansion."

Billy had no choice. There was no use ARGUING — his uncle would hound him about it for DAYS! So he put on his BEST suit and tie and got ready to meet the triplets.

There! Now you're ready for dinner at the Rattenbaum Mansion.

FILTHY RICH OR JUST PRETENDING?

Billy rang the BELL of the Rattenbaum Mansion. He expected to hear the sound of musical chimes. Instead, he heard an earsplitting clattering sound, like a bunch of pots and pans banging together.

BANG BANG BANG BANG BANG BANG BANG

Billy jumped back and screamed loudly. Then he realized it was just the bell. Embarrassed, he looked around, hoping

nobody had seen him acting like a scaredy-mouse.

The outside of the mansion was dark, SILENT, and empty. A few scraggly trees covered in GREEN mold stuck up here and there. THORNY bushes wrapped around the tree trunks. The decorative columns on top of the mansion's towers looked like they were going to collapse at any moment. Loose window shutters banged back and forth in the wind.

"I must have the wrong address," Billy muttered. "This house looks like it's been deserted for years!"

He was about to leave when he heard an eerie creak and the door slowly opened. Then a gray PAW reached through the doorway, grabbed him by the collar, and dragged him inside.

vase about to fall

pped
cco

dried-up
plant

RATTENBAUM MANSION

17 Twilight Way
Gloomeria, Mysterious Valley

All original documents have been lost, but tradition tells us that the construction of this mansion began in 1313. The great Rattonzio Rattenbaum demanded a dwelling worthy of the strength and power of the Rattenbaum name. Over the years, Rattonzio's descendants have worked constantly to keep the mansion in its original glory. To date, there have been 217 refurbishments, 513 redesigns, 778 renovations, 471 reconstructions, 228 upgrades, 1,213 reductions, and 215 adjustments.

Lately, however, the present members of the Rattenbaum family decided to stop all renovations. Officially, they did this to preserve the history of the mansion. Unofficially, they did it because they ran out of money.

We do not suggest visiting the mansion because of the high possibility of falling ceilings, walls, and columns.

"Hurry up! Get in! You're letting in the **COLD**!" snapped the gray-furred rodent. Do you know how much heating costs these days?"

Billy found himself in a **chilly** and dark entrance hall, snout-to-snout with a bizarre-looking rodent. He wore a black suit that had once been **ELEGANT**, but was now covered with patches. A squashed top hat sat on his head.

"Good day, Master Bobby," the rodent said. "*Welcome* to our superluxurious mansion!"

"Actually, my name is Billy," the author corrected him.

Shamley Rattenbaum

The gray rodent ignored him. "I am Shamley Rattenbaum, lord of the mansion! And these are my wonderful, marvelous, **enchanting** granddaughters."

Three rodents in evening gowns emerged from the shadows.

"Hi, I'm Tilly!"

"Hi, I'm Milly!"

"Hi, I'm Lilly!"

Billy cleared his throat and politely introduced himself.

"Ahem. Pleased to meet you. I am —"

Tilly interrupted him. "We know who you are!"

"Of course we do!" added Milly.

"We know EVERYTHING about you!" said Lilly.

I'm Tilly!

I'm Milly!

I'm Lilly!

"Of course, you know my granddaughters are HIGH-SOCIETY rodents," Shamley bragged. "In fact, they couldn't be any more HIGH SOCIETY than they are now."

Then he leaned toward Billy. They were so close their whiskers were touching.

"How about you?" he asked. "Are you a DUKE? Maybe a COUNT?"

Billy didn't know what to say. The Rattenbaums seemed to be obsessed with royalty!

"Let me guess," said Shamley. "You're a prince, right? I can tell just by looking at you!"

"Yes! I see it in your UNCOMBED fur!" exclaimed Tilly.

"Yes! I see it in your CROOKED whiskers!" added Milly.

"Yes! I see it in your WRINKLY clothes!" concluded Lilly.

Shamley grabbed Billy by the collar again.

"Let's go! We can find your history upstairs."

The rodent pulled Billy down the dismal **HALL**. Dingy paintings of grouchy-looking rodents covered the walls.

"Here are the paintings of all of our HIGH-SOCIETY ancestors," Shamley said proudly. "We are the OLDEST family in the Valley. It's all in the Book."

"The B-Book?" Billy stammered.

"*Follow* me and you'll see for yourself!" said Shamley with a gleam in his eyes.

THE BOOK

Shamley stopped in front of a massive wooden **door** with a great big padlock on the knob. He searched his pockets and took out a **key**. Then he fiddled with the lock until the door opened.

Behind that door was another door secured with a **CHAIN** and another lock. He opened that door to reveal a third small door with thirteen **DEAD BOLTS**. He opened the locks one by one. Finally, he pulled open the door and Billy saw a room behind it.

"Come!" he told Billy. "It's time to consult the Book!"

The timid mouse cautiously followed

Shamley inside. The large room was filled with dusty objects that looked like they'd been around since the dawn of time. But the biggest item in the room was a truly **ENORMOUSE** book propped up on a stand.

Shamley climbed up a tall ladder, fixed his **EYEGLASSES** on the tip of his snout, and began to turn the huge pages.

"Let's see . . . Squeakino . . . Squeaksley . . . Squeakstail . . . Hmm. I can't seem to find you," he said.

Billy was puzzled. "What are you **LOOKING** for?"

"Your name, of course!" Shamley replied. "The Book has the names of all of the royal and high-society rodents in Mysterious Valley. It also has a family tree for each name. Every lord, lady, count, countess, duke, duchess, prince, and princess is in here."

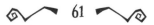

Mechanical page-turner

Book stand

"Why should my name be here?" Billy asked.

"It's obvious! Because you're a NOBLE. Otherwise, how could I let you marry one of my VERY NOBLE granddaughters?"

"What? 'Marry'?" Billy cried. *"Bouncing bookmarks!* **I DON'T WANT TO GET MARRIED!**"

Shamley pretended not to hear him. "Does your name have a C in it, by any chance?"

"Of course not!" Billy said.

"A Z ?" Shamley asked.

"Not that, either."

"How about a double X ?" Shamley tried.

Billy sighed. "Not that, either!"

"Hmm. Let me take another look," Shamley told him.

No matter how hard he tried, Shamley could not find Billy's name in the Book. But that didn't bother him. He took a **pencil**

from his pocket. "I can just make a little addition here," he muttered to himself. He wrote a name in the Book.

Bobby Squeekspir

"Look! I found proof!" Shamley cried. "You're a noble! High society from the tip of your noble nose to the end of your noble tail."

He **JUMPED** down from the ladder and hugged Billy. *"Welcome to our family!"*

Billy tried to get out of Shamley's grasp.

"It's always a pleasure to greet a **G-U-E-S-T** like you," Shamley added.

Once again, Billy was puzzled. Why was Shamley spelling out words?

His host explained. "And by **G**-**U**-**E**-**S**-**T** I mean **G**ive **U**s **E**xcellent **S**upport **T**oday." Shamley cleared his throat. "As you can see, the magnificent design of this mansion is in need of some **REPAIR**."

"*Some* repair?" Billy asked. "This place is a **DISASTER** area!" Right above his head, a tile was about to fall from the ceiling.

At that moment, a nasal voice ECHOED ECHOED throughout the mansion. ECHOED

"The butler is happy to announce that DINNER is being served!"

THE INVISIBLE DINNER

The **ENTIRE** Rattenbaum family was seated around the rickety table in the dining room.

Lady Fifi, the triplets' grandmother, wore a dress that was the height of fashion — fifty years ago. Now it was covered in **Patches**. She walked over to Billy and held out her paw for a kiss.

"En-enchanted, my lady," Billy said, giving a **CLUMSY** bow.

"Finally!" she exclaimed. "It's been years since we've had a GENTLEMOUSE as a guest. Tonight, we are serving a very **SPECIAL** dinner in your honor."

Shamley nudged one of his granddaughters. "Milly, bring us the menu!"

"Grandfather, I'm Tilly!" she protested.

"Sorry, my little *cheesenip*," her grandfather said sweetly. "You are all so much alike."

Tilly handed Billy a **TATTERED** menu. "Here it is. It's the latest fashion in high society: INVISIBLE dinner!"

INVISIBLE DINNER

APPETIZERS
VERY LIGHT CRACKERS
(So light they blew away!)
CHEESE BALL MADE OF AIR

FIRST COURSE
SEAWEED SOUP FROM A SEA THAT DOESN'T EXIST
WITH MEMORIES OF PASTA FROM DAYS PAST

SECOND COURSE
FILET OF RARE FISH
(So rare we were not able to find it!)
WITH AROMAS OF FORGOTTEN CHEESE

DESSERT
FANTASY CAKE
(Fantasize your favorite flavor and then imagine eating it.)

BEVERAGES
AN ASSORTMENT OF INVISIBLE JUICES
THAT HAVE NO TASTE

The butler began to serve dinner. Billy noticed he was also the messenger from earlier that day. There was NOTHING on his serving tray, and the dishes remained EMPTY. But the Rattenbaums were excited about every serving.

"How delicious!" the rodents exclaimed each time.

"Dear Shamley, please pour me some more of that juice," said Lady Fifi. "It's so refreshing."

Shamley lifted the empty pitcher and pretended to pour something into his wife's glass. Billy was STUNNED. Who ever heard of an invisible dinner? But most of all, he was hungry!

Just then, his cell phone rang.

Riiiiiiiing Riiiiiiiing Riiiiiiiing

Billy was glad to have an excuse to leave the table. He quickly made his escape to another room.

"**Hello, Billy-Willy?**" asked the voice at the other end.

"Creepella? Is that you?" Billy asked.

"Of course it's me!" she replied. "Are you home? How are the **13 GHOSTS**?"

"No, actually I'm . . ."

Creepella interrupted him. "It doesn't matter. I'm on a case and I need your help."

"A c-case?" Billy asked.

"Right!" she answered. "This case is very **MYSTERIOUS**. I asked the advice of a monster expert . . . but there's no time to talk. Meet me in front of Horrorwood Studios at the stroke of **MIDNIGHT**!"

"Th-the stroke of midnight?" That idea spooked Billy. But Creepella had already hung up.

The triplets caught up to him, SURROUNDING him.

"Bobby —" Tilly began.

"— who —" Milly continued

"— was that?" Lilly finished.

"That was my friend Creepella von Cacklefur," Billy replied. "Do you know her?"

The triplets began to **SOB** hysterically.

"Wh-what's wrong?" Billy asked.

"Don't mention that FLIRT!" Tilly said with a sigh.

"She's so UNPLEASANT!" Milly said with a sniff.

"And such a SHOW-OFF!" Lilly said with a sob.

Lady Fifi approached them. "Did I hear correctly, Count Bobby? Are you leaving us?"

Billy nodded. "Actually, I have another appointment. I have to go to the MOVIE STUDIOS."

"Then I hope you will bring the girls with you," said Lady Fifi.

"Yes!" the triplets cried happily.

Billy gave up. He left the mansion with the three girls. They made a quick stop at his house so he could change his clothes. Then they headed toward Horrorwood Studios.

Fantastic!

Hooray!

Yes!

A Mysterious Midnight Meeting

"*Shrieks and Monsters*, scene sixteen, take one!" Sam Shivers yelled. "**Action!**"

The director had decided to shoot a scene without Blobbina in it. He was hoping the star of his film would appear before long. If not, his movie would be RUINED!

Billy entered the studio with the Rattenbaum triplets. The girls ran to Shivers, bubbling over with excitement.

"We want —" Tilly began.

"— to be —" Milly continued.

"— in your movie!" Lilly finished.

The director raised an eyebrow.

"Hmm," he said. "I might have a small part for you as extras."

The girls squealed with delight. "We're going to be actors!"

"I want a TRAILER all to myself," said Tilly.

"A golden dressing room for me," said Milly.

"A team of makeup artists just for me," added Lilly.

Just then, the studio clock began to toll midnight. Billy left the triplets with Sam Shivers and went to find Creepella.

I can't — wait — to start!

"Billy-Willy!" Creepella called out to him. "There you are. We must start the **INVESTIGATION** right away."

"What's going on?" Billy asked. "Why are we here so late?"

"Gorgo, our moat monster, is **IN LOVE** with Blobbina, Horrorwood's greatest star," Creepella explained quickly. "But she **DISAPPEARED**. And our monster expert—"

"M-monster expert?" Billy stammered.

"That's right," Creepella said. "Mr. M. is the greatest **MONSTER** expert in Mysterious Valley. He told me to be here exactly at **MIDNIGHT**. He sent me a note."

First Clue:
Horrorwood Studios,
Midnight!

Mr. M.

"What does this have to do with me?" Billy asked.

"I need a partner on this case," Creepella explained. *"Let's go!"*

The whole plan scared Billy. "Wh-where?"

Then he heard the gloomy sound of a funeral march. Creepella's cell phone was ringing.

"It's a message from Mr. M.!"

SECOND CLUE:
NIGHTMARE PARK...
MR. M.

"Wh-what's Nightmare Park?" Billy asked nervously.

"It's a **FANTASTIC** place!" Creepella replied. "It's an old amousement park on the eastern wing of the studios. Nobody ever goes there anymore."

"So why should *we* go there?" Billy asked.

"To solve this MYSTERY!" she answered. She grabbed his arm and began to drag him toward the park.

Wh-where are we going?

To solve this mystery!

WATCH WHERE YOU PUT YOUR PAWS!

They followed the *path* to the east wing of Horrorwood Studios. They soon found themselves facing the huge walls of ‹NIGHTMARE PARK›. They pushed open the massive METAL doors, which closed behind them with a loud clang.

They looked around and saw they were in a thick FOREST. The path in front of them forked in several directions.

Billy scratched his head. "Which way do we go now?" he asked as he *LEANED* against the nearest tree.

BADA BAM!

The tree crashed to the ground. Billy grabbed helplessly at the empty air, but then he, too, fell with a thud.

"Billy, you're so clumsy!" Creepella scolded. "You toppled a prop!"

Billy stood up, dazed. "Prop?"

"These aren't real trees," she said. "They're PAINTED panels!"

"BOUNCING bookmarks!" Billy exclaimed. He looked behind another tree. It was completely flat! "Is the entire forest fake?"

"The Dark Forest was one of the biggest attractions in Nightmare Park," Creepella explained. Then she pointed.

"And down there is the Black Lake! See? The water is as black as **INK**."

She inched closer to him. "They filmed the blockbuster *Tentacles, Tentacles* in that lake."

Frightened, Billy took a step backward. He tripped and his paw hit a **BUTTON** hidden between the rocks. The water in the lake began to boil and bubble. From the center of the lake, a **MYSTERIOUS TENTACLE** wriggled out like a giant snake. It slithered toward Billy and grabbed him by the ankle.

"Heeeeeeellllllllllppppppppp!"

Billy cried. The monstrous tentacle dangled him **UPSIDE DOWN** over the lake and shook him to and fro. He opened his mouth to scream again, but he froze when he found himself staring at two large, **EVIL-LOOKING** green eyes.

"Billy, please don't waste time playing with the **GIANT OCTOPUS**," Creepella scolded. "We've got a mystery to solve!"

"Heeelp meeee!"

Billy screamed.

Creepella chuckled. "I'll turn it off," she said. She walked around the lake to the panel that controlled the robot octopus. She pressed the first button she saw. The octopus's tentacles began to wave faster and faster!

"**I'm getting seasick!**" Billy cried.

"Whoops! I'll try this one," Creepella said, pressing another **BUTTON**.

The octopus stopped for a moment. Then it started to tickle Billy with the tips of its tentacles. Billy couldn't stop laughing.

"Ha ha ha! Hee hee hee! Ho ho ho!"

Creepella placed her hands on her hips. "This is nothing to laugh about, Billy! We're wasting precious time!"

She impatiently pressed the third **BUTTON** on the panel. The octopus finally stopped moving and let go of Billy.

Splash!

Billy swam back to the shore as fast as his arms could get him there.

"Why, oh why, didn't I stay home?" he wailed.

THE LAST CLUE

Creepella stomped away from the lake. "I can't always wait for you, Billy!" she called behind her.

"Wait!" he shouted, wringing out his **SOGGY** clothes. "Don't leave me here alone!"

He tried to catch up to her, but he tripped on something and landed once again with his snout in the **GRASS**.

"Let's try that trail," Creepella said, pointing to a narrow **GRAVEL** path. "What do you think, Billy? Billy? Where did you go?"

"UMPF BFRT!"

Billy replied through a mouthful of grass.

"I can't believe it! You fell again?" Creepella asked.

"Yes, but . . . *pffft!*" Billy spit out a clover. "I tripped on a magnifying glass. People will leave anything lying around, won't they?"

"Let me see that!" Creepella bent down. "There's a NOTE from Mr. M. here!"

Look where you
put your paws!
Mr. M.

Creepella grabbed the magnifying glass. She walked down the *path*, carefully examining the ground before she took each step. Soon she saw a pink STAIN on the gravel.

"That looks like pink SLIME!" she exclaimed. "Let's keep following it."

Billy kept pace behind her. After a few more steps they saw a row of pink tentacle P R I N T S that veered off of the path.

"Those must be Blobbina's tracks!" remarked Creepella,

pleased with the discovery.

They followed the tracks down a new path. Billy saw nothing but darkness ahead. Then he made out the shadow of a GLOOMY castle. A feeble light shone from the castle's highest tower.

"L-let's go home," Billy said, his teeth chattering from fright.

But Creepella was already running ahead.

She stopped in front of a large drawbridge that looked very unsteady. The moat below was so deep and murky that she couldn't see the bottom. Here and there, yellow SLANTED EYES peeked out of the dark water. Then the sound of chomping TEETH filled the night air.

Billy caught up to her. "Wh-what is that?" he asked.

"crocodiles, I think," Creepella replied calmly. She crossed the bridge, and Billy followed her, his tail twitching with fear.

They entered the castle. The only light inside came from the full moon shining through the windows.

"I saw a light up in the tower," Creepella said. "Let's go there!"

A long and narrow staircase led to the top.

Creepella took the steps two at a time. Billy SCRAMBLED to keep up with her, breathing heavily. Through the small windows in the tower wall he could see the forest down below.

"L-looks like we're going up very high," he said nervously. "I think we should s-stop here."

"You aren't afraid of **HEIGHTS**, are you, Billy-Willy?" Creepella asked. "Wait until I take you to the top of Bitewing's tower in Cacklefur Castle. The view there will take your breath away!"

"Actually . . . *puff* . . . *pant* . . . I'm already out of *breath*!" Billy pointed out.

They CLIMBED . . . and CLIMBED . . . and CLIMBED. Finally, they reached the room in the top of the tower. It was a small room with stone walls.

"Wh-what's that in the middle of the room?" Billy asked. "It looks like a casket!"

"In fact, it's a CASKET made of crystal," Creepella said. "Let's take a look!"

Billy looked at the see-through walls of the casket and jumped back. Two huge eyes with long EYELASHES were staring at him!

Creepella wasn't afraid. She lifted the lid of the casket and a pink GELATINOUS monster slithered out.

"BLOBBINA!" Creepella cried. "It's you!"

Billy was confused. "This is B-Blobbina? I thought we were looking for a movie star, not a monster!"

"She is a MOVIE STAR — the most MONSTROUS star in the Valley, and we've finally found her!" Creepella exclaimed happily.

KIDNAPPED!

Billy stepped back from the pink slime on the floor, a look of **DISGUST** on his face. But Creepella thought Blobbina was beautiful. She talked to the monster in her own language.

"*Bluuuup! Blu blu blu bluuuuuŘp!*" gurgled Blobbina.

"*Bluřp?*" asked Creepella

"*Blup!*" answered the monster.

Billy was *astonished*. "Do you really understand her?" he asked.

"**OF COURSE!**" Creepella replied.

"MONSTERIAN is taught to all the children in Gloomeria at a very early age. It's tradition!"

Blobbina let out a heart-wrenching moan.

"Oh, poor thing!" Creepella exclaimed. "She told me she was KIDNAPPED by the evil Dr. Inkubus."

"D-Doctor who?" Billy stammered.

"He is the old **caretaker** of Nightmare Park," Creepella explained. "It used to be the star attraction of Horrorwood Studios. Oh, I remember the time I rode the marvelous

Upside-Down Merry-Go-Round!

But the park shut down right after that."

"I'm not surprised," Billy sniffed. "It really seems like a **HORRIBLE** place!"

DOCTOR INKUBUS

WHO HE IS: An expert in creating nightmares, shivers, goose bumps, and screams of fright.

WHERE HE LIVES: Since the park closed, he hides in a dark and secret corner of Horrorwood Studios. It is said he only comes out at night.

EDUCATION: He has a degree from Shivery Arts Academy. He majored in Screams, Shrieks, and Screeches.

HOBBY: He collects recordings of the most bloodcurdling screams in horror films.

HIS DREAM: To bring Nightmare Park back to its original splendor, with the same hair-raising attractions it had years ago.

"On the contrary, the horribleness of the place was a big draw," Creepella said. "But after a few years, people stopped getting scared. So the park was abandoned."

Blobbina interrupted her.

"Bluppp blurept blu blub!"

"She said Dr. Inkubus dreams of reopening the park," Creepella translated.

"Blup bluup blu!"

"And he wants to force Blobbina to be the main attraction!" Creepella finished.

"Blup!" moaned Blobbina. A pink TEAR ran down her cheek.

"Poor thing," Creepella said. "She belongs on the big screen, not IMPRISONED in an amusement park! We need to get her out of here!"

Creepella quickly dialed Cacklefur Castle on her cell phone.

"Boneham! There's an **EMERGENCY**!" she said. "Hurry to NIGHTMARE PARK'S entrance. And bring the sidecar. You know, the one we use to bring Gorgo to the **SWAMP**."

She ended the call and turned to Billy. "We have to get out of here! You go first, Blobbina will follow you, and I'll bring up the rear."

"Where do you think you're going?"

Creepella turned and saw the SKELETAL shadow of Dr. Inkubus behind them.

"HE'S ONTO US!" she cried.

Blobbina slithered faster and bumped into Billy. The two of them rolled down the stairs together in a blur of **PINK SLIME**. Only Billy's head and paws peeked out from the gelatinous goo.

Creepella ran after them.

"*HURRY!*" she yelled.

She gave the ball of slime a big shove, sending Blobbina and Billy tumbling out of the castle and *sliding* down the path. Dr. Inkubus chased them, shouting, "Get back here! **That monster is miiiiiiiiiiine!**"

But he didn't get far. **BAM!** He slipped on a **BLOB** of pink slime and ended up flat on his back with his paws in the air.

NIGHTMARE PARK

The strange trio arrived at the park entrance to find Boneham on a motorcycle, honking the horn **loudly**. Creepella pushed the pink monster into the sidecar and jumped on the seat. Billy was still stuck inside the glob of pink GOO!

"Step on it!" Creepella yelled. "To Cacklefur Castle!"

We did it!

WEDDING BELLS AT CACKLEFUR CASTLE

The sun was rising over the **HORIZON**, brightening the sky over Mysterious Valley when Boneham's motorcycle stopped in front of Cacklefur Castle. He honked the horn several times, and the von Cacklefur family all came outside.

"Welcome back, Creepella!"

Bitewing cried. He pointed his wings toward Blobbina. "What is that **weird** creature?"

"It's Blobbina! We found her!" Creepella told everyone. "She was kidnapped by Dr. Inkubus."

"How unusual," said Boris von Cacklefur.

"Blobbina has a rodent's whiskers and a tail."

"Oh, that's just silly Billy Squeakspeare," Creepella explained. "Blobbina fell on him and he got trapped."

"BLECH!" shrieked Billy, as he set himself free from the slimy pink monster.

Then the moat began to BUBBLE. Two surprised love-struck eyes stared out of the mud at Blobbina.

It was Gorgo.

"BlUUY!" gurgled Gorgo happily when he saw Blobbina.

Blech!

"Blirp!" Blobbina answered, batting her eyelashes.

Grandma Crypt sighed loudly and held her hands over her heart.

"AH, LOVE..."

Boris nodded. "The two of them are made for each other. Just look at them!"

Shivereen ran to Creepella, holding a piece of paper. "Auntie, this just arrived! It's from **Mr. M.**"

Billy took a **BACKWARD STEP**. "W-well, it's time for me to go," he said. But a **PAW** grabbed him by the sleeve.

"No, no, my Billy-Willy," said Creepella. "You can't leave now. You have to stay here for the **rehearsal**!"

Congratulations!

You have brilliantly solved the case (thanks to my clues, of course!) For now, at least, the Valley is safe from evil Dr. Inkubus and his wicked plans. Blobbina is safe. Besides . . . well, you already know. She and Gorgo have been in love for some time! I believe that soon there will be a beautiful wedding at Cacklefur Castle.

Please send me the photos for my next book, <u>Monstrously Romantic Moments</u>.

SINCERELY,
MR. M.

"R-rehearsal?" Billy stammered.

"Yes, the wedding rehearsal," Creepella said. "You can be Gorgo's BEST MAN, and I'll be Blobbina's maid of honor!"

Billy fainted on the spot, but the ring of his cell phone quickly woke him up. The Rattenbaum triplets had left him a message.

"Bobby, where are you?" they whined. "We got you a part in the movie. You have to lower yourself by the thread of a spider's web into the Bottomless Well! Aren't you happy?"

Billy fainted again. Meanwhile, Grandpa Frankenstein brought a pail filled with old, rusted screws to the moat.

"Our GORGO seems happy now," he said. "But let's test just to make sure."

He threw the pail of rusty screws into the moat. Gorgo gobbled up every last one. He

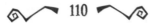

ate everything but the handle, which was too clean and new for him. He spit it out — and it hit Billy right in the face! The poor writer, who was just beginning to come to, **fainted** for the third time.

"**Gorgo is better!**"

Creepella cheered. "It's a happy ending to a scary story — the perfect story to send to my friend *Geronimo Stilton*!"

THE END

THE NEWEST SENSATION IN HORROR!

After I finished reading Creepella's book, Bitewing chuckled.

"Good story, right? So, did you figure out who's getting **married?**" the bat asked me.

"Of course," I answered. "The two **MONSTERS** of Mysterious Valley: Gorgo and Blobbina!"

"Exactly!" the bat snickered. "That's why I brought you this tombstone-shaped **WEDDING** invitation. You're invited! Are you ready to go?"

"Hmm . . . a wedding between monsters?"

I said with a shiver. "**Brrr!** My whiskers are curling from fright!"

Bitewing fluttered around my head. "No excuses! The trip is already booked. But before you go, you have to publish this **BOOK** . . . **_PRONTO!_** In fact, Creepella's already working on her next one."

I couldn't argue with the bat. It's clear to me that Mysterious Valley is home to a truly fabumouse author of SCARY STORIES . . .

CREEPELLA VON CACKLEFUR!

If you liked this book, be sure
to check out my next adventure!

GHOST PIRATE TREASURE

Oh, no! Billy Squeakspeare has a big problem,
and he needs Creepella's help. Someone's been
digging holes around Squeakspeare Mansion at
night, and Billy wants to find out who it is. The
dangerous, legendary pirate Morgan Darkwhisker
is said to have buried his long-lost treasure near
Squeakspeare Mansion years ago—could he be
hunting for his hidden riches? It's up to Billy and
Creepella to find the treasure first!

And don't miss any of my other fabumouse adventures!

#1 Lost Treasure of the Emerald Eye

#2 The Curse of the Cheese Pyramid

#3 Cat and Mouse in a Haunted House

#4 I'm Too Fond of My Fur!

#5 Four Mice Deep in the Jungle

#6 Paws Off, Cheddarface!

#7 Red Pizzas for a Blue Count

#8 Attack of the Bandit Cats

#9 A Fabumouse Vacation for Geronimo

#10 All Because of a Cup of Coffee

#11 It's Halloween, You 'Fraidy Mouse!

#12 Merry Christmas, Geronimo!

#13 The Phantom of the Subway

#14 The Temple of the Ruby of Fire

#15 The Mona Mousa Code

#16 A Cheese-Colored Camper

#17 Watch Your Whiskers, Stilton!

#18 Shipwreck on the Pirate Islands

#19 My Name Is Stilton, Geronimo Stilton

#20 Surf's Up, Geronimo!

#21 The Wild, Wild West

#22 The Secret of Cacklefur Castle

A Christmas T

#23 Valentine's Day Disaster

#24 Field Trip to Niagara Falls

#25 The Search for Sunken Treasure

#26 The Mummy with No Name

#27 The Christmas To Factory

#28 Wedding Crasher

#29 Down and Out Down Under

#30 The Mouse Island Marathon

#31 The Mysterious Cheese Thief

Christmas Catastrophe

#32 Valley of the Giant Skeletons

#33 Geronimo and the Gold Medal Mystery

#34 Geronimo Stilton, Secret Agent

#35 A Very Merry Christmas

#36 Geronim Valentine

37 The Race
ross America

#38 A Fabumouse
School Adventure

#39 Singing
Sensation

#40 The Karate
Mouse

#41 Mighty
Mount
Kilimanjaro

2 The Peculiar
umpkin Thief

#43 I'm Not a
Supermouse!

#44 The Giant
Diamond Robbery

#45 Save the
White Whale!

#46 The Haunted
Castle

And coming soon!

#47 Run for the Hills,
Geronimo!

1. Mountains of the Mangy Yeti
2. Cacklefur Castle
3. Angry Walnut Tree
4. Rattenbaum Palace
5. Rancidrat River
6. Bridge of Shaky Steps
7. Squeakspeare Mansion
8. Slimy Swamp
9. Ogre Highway
10. Gloomeria
11. Shivery Arts Academy
12. Horrorwood Studios

CACKLEFUR CASTLE

1. Oozing moat

2. Drawbridge

3. Grand entrance

4. Moldy basement

5. Patio, with a view of the moat

6. Dusty library

7. Room for unwanted guests

8. Mummy room

9. Watchtower

10. Creaking staircase

11. Banquet room

12. Garage (for antique hearses)

13. Bewitched tower

14. Garden of carnivorous plants

15. Stinky kitchen

16. Crocodile pool and piranha tank

17. Creepella's room

18. Tower of musky tarantulas

19. Bitewing's tower (with antique contraptions)

DEAR MOUSE FRIENDS,
GOOD-BYE UNTIL
THE NEXT BOOK!